SCOTLAND

A REWILDING JOURNEY

"Man is faced with a choice between two values: material worth and spiritual worth. Material worth is fickle, transient, unenduring; it is also discriminatory, offering privilege to the few while keeping opportunity from the many. Matters of the spirit are known to every single human being, the very pivot of the heart."

V S Pritchett

First published in 2018 by SCOTLAND: The Big Picture
Reprinted in 2021 (with updated text)
www.scotlandbigpicture.com

Written by Susan Wright and Peter Cairns
(except chapter 6 written by Nick Underdown)

Images: Peter Cairns, Mark Hamblin, James Shooter, Richard
Shucksmith, Philip Price, Guy Richardson, Laurent Geslin, Ronan Dugan,
Aidan Maccormick

All images are held within the SCOTLAND: The Big Picture image
library and are available for licensing upon request, subject to
appropriate reproduction fees.

Infographics by Claire Proctor: www.hill99design.co.uk
Artwork by Phil Mumby and Matt Lissimore: www.scotlandbigpicture.com
Wild Words artwork by Gemma Wright: www.scotlandbigpicture.com

Project management by Peter Cairns: www.scotlandbigpicture.com
Book production by Mark Hamblin: www.scotlandbigpicture.com
Book design by Adam Alexander: www.coirecreative.co.uk
Text editing by Gordon Eaglesham and Polly Pullar:
www.scotlandbigpicture.com

Colour reproduction by Pixel Colour Imaging: www.pixelcolourimaging.com
Printed and bound in Italy by Printer Trento: www.printertrento.it

The Forest Stewardship Council ® (FSC) is an independent, not
for profit, non-government organization established to support
environmentally appropriate, socially beneficial, and economically viable
management of the world's forests.

This book is made with paper from responsible sources and meets the
eligibility requirements stipulated by the FSC.

ISBN: 978-0-9568423-3-6

Contents

Rewilding: Nothing to be afraid of...

We are living in a time when one species - Homo sapiens (humans) - is having such an impact on the planet that geologists have declared it a new era in the history of the earth. We live in the 'Anthropocene' and it started just 12,000 years ago. A mere second in the 4.5 billion-year history of the earth.

But what changes we have made in that short amount of time. The moment the first fire was lit by people, we were able to shape the world around us, and as we began to harness nature through keeping animals and growing plants, the world became less 'natural' and more under the control of people. Gradually, but ever-more quickly, the great wilderness areas of the world have been lost.

This is not to say that other species do not shape the world around them too. Trees produce leaves that fall and decay to build up fertile soil where once there was bare rock. Wolves have famously changed the landscape of the Yellowstone National Park by frightening their prey so trees now grow where once it was grassland. These are natural processes and have enabled the planet to function to support all life on earth.

Trees for Life believes there is a place on the earth for natural processes to take precedence over human intervention. Our founder, Alan Watson Featherstone, has championed 'ecological restoration' since the 1980s and we have pioneered the restoration of the once widespread Caledonian forest of the Highlands of Scotland since then.

Without human intervention, natural processes would result in much of the Highlands being covered in a diverse forest. Imagine Scots pine with juniper and silver birch on the colder mountainsides and oak forest with primroses and bluebells in the warmer areas. Imagine a natural treeline where tall trees give way to stunted willows and birches, marking the edge of the forest. Among this would still be deep peat bogs in the wettest areas and rocky, alpine habitats on the highest mountains. It would still be Highland Scotland, but not quite as we know it.

The work of Trees for Life so far has been about preparing the landscape for a time when natural processes can take over. This has involved planting trees in a bare landscape behind fences to provide a seed source for the future. Trees are planted behind fences because the current high numbers of grazing animals would prevent them from growing. It has also included reducing the numbers of wild deer in some areas so that trees can grow naturally from seed. Both methods enable new trees to grow, which is the first stage of forest restoration. This has been very successful and you can see the results for yourself in Glen Affric and at Dundreggan.

However, a restored forest is more than the trees. The matrix of plants, animals, fungi and micro-organisms that make up the forest is what enable natural processes to strike a balance so all life can flourish within it. Some species are especially important. Jays and red squirrels are crucial because they collect seeds and nuts that they store in the ground and then forget about, inadvertently planting the next generation of trees in the process. Beavers build dams and harvest trees, creating ponds that hold back floodwater and provide places where fish and dragonflies can thrive. Wolves and lynx move grazing animals around by harassing, stalking and hunting them, allowing young trees to grow when otherwise they would be eaten.

We have taken the first small steps in rebuilding the forest matrix by reintroducing red squirrels to forests they have been lost from in the Northwest Highlands. They are rapidly recolonising these areas, helping to bring back a key component of what a naturally functioning forest would be. Trees for Life is encouraging the reintroduction of beaver to the Highlands and we also advocate the return of other missing species such as lynx, when the time is right.

This ecological restoration of a once widespread forest is something that Trees for Life began more than 25 years ago. We pioneered the concept that land could be restored and natural processes should take charge, because we believe there is room in Scotland, and ultimately 'nature knows best'. Rewilding as it is now called was initially unpopular and controversial, but now more landowners, conservationists and scientists are realising that allowing nature to be in charge makes good sense and does not have to be in conflict with other priorities.

One of the reasons rewilding has been seen as a threat is the fear that it will take away jobs and livelihoods in rural communities that already struggle to provide work for young people, leading to yet more depopulation. There is also a fear that traditional rural pastimes, like deer stalking, would end as the land becomes ever-more covered in forest.

Nothing could be further from the truth, because humans can be part of natural processes too, as long as we do not dominate the rest of nature. A restored matrix of forest, moorland, mountain top and bog will provide more employment in the Highlands, partly because people want to see and experience wild nature. Other rewilding projects in Europe show how they help to ensure that young people who might otherwise leave, can stay if there are interesting and desirable jobs for them. The jobs created by nature-based tourism are often just that. So too are modernised versions of traditional rural work, taking what we need from the land, but not destroying it in the process.

One staunch advocate of rewilding once told me the reason he wants to see it happen is because he can imagine a time when there will be more and better hunting opportunities. He imagines a time when he will be shooting bigger red deer, but also lost creatures like wild boar and even, one day, wolves. It is an unpalatable truth to many that hunting can be an important part of securing the future of a reintroduced species.

Trees for Life wants to play a full and transformational part in this exciting journey. Our agenda is unashamedly about restoring the Caledonian forest and returning the lost species so that natural processes can take over. But we are not arrogant about it. We realise that landowners and communities want, what might seem on the surface, to be very different things. But we believe that by talking and working together we will see a time when the Highlands of Scotland will be wilder, with more people making a living from this wonderful land, while those that enjoy the traditional pleasures of this special place feel a part of the changing landscape and not excluded from it.

Our first steps on this new pathway are just beginning as this landmark book is being published. Trees for Life is working with the landowning community to examine the remnants of ancient pinewood that remain so we can work out how to grow a new forest from them. We are also training the next generation of people who will work in the Highlands so they can combine traditional land management techniques with rewilding skills. We are talking with landowners, communities and businesses about how the vision of a rewilded landscape can deliver what they want from the land too. As always, people are part of the solution, we just need to find a way to take our place with the other species that should share this wonderful landscape with us.

Steve Micklewright

Chief Executive, Trees for Life

Partners

SCOTLAND: A Rewilding Journey has been made possible through the generous support of the following partner organisations. All of them are working to create a wilder Scotland in their own way, but have come together with Trees for Life and SCOTLAND: The Big Picture to enable this book to encourage more people to help make rewilding a reality.

www.rewildingbritain.org.uk

www.reforestingscotland.org

www.treesforlife.org.uk

www.bordersforesttrust.org

www.scotlandbigpicture.com

www.rewildingeurope.com

www.theeuropeannaturetrust.com

www.woodlandtrust.org.uk

Thanks

The following individuals and organisations kindly contributed to a crowdfunding campaign to support the publication of this book.

Supporters

Adam Fry, Andrew MacAoidh Jergens, Audrey Hughes, Berny and Cleo Welsh, Bryan Moore, Caroline, Cheryl Surry, David Geddes, David Scott, Deb, Deborah Lewis, Douglas A Peacock, Douglas Gooday, DR Robert, D S Sanderson, Emilia Leese, Emma Kareno and Henning Hoeber, Ewan Sandison, George Christelis, HAGGIS Adventures, Grant Macfarlane, Guy Johnson, Hans Karlsborn, Helen Miller, Helen Senn, Hugo van Vredenburch, Ian Boyd-Livingston, Isobel and Michael Scarborough, James Meiklejohn, Jay Hooke, Joanna Caird, Jonathan Philp, Julie Ellis, Kaori Camplese, Kathryn Robertson, Laura Mazzara, Laurent Cocherel, Linda Carruthers, Lorenzo Dutto, Macnaughton Family, Malcolm Sievwright, Mark Hoogenboom, Marlies MacLean, Mary McElwee, Mary Peart, Montha Cheng, Nathalie Siv, Patricia Mang, Chithiphot Cheng, Nicholas Griffiths, Nick Campbell, Nigel Fraser, Noah Gibbs, Patrick Rainey, Paul Hibberd, Peter Edge, Richard Martinez, Richard Morley, Rob Schulze, Simon Whalley, Steve Thomas, Steven O'Keeffe, Stevie McPhail, Stewart McLellan, Stuart Marpole, Suzanne Rice, Tom White, Ur Wald Fund, Walter de Sagher.

Key Supporters

Alan Bonnyman, Ben Goldsmith, Daphne Such, Ivy Kapur, Peter Keiller

Welcome to Scotland

SCOTLAND
80,077 km²

| **282** Munros | **31,000** freshwater lochs | **220** sea lochs | **15,000 km** of coastline |

HIGHLANDS & ISLANDS
40,500 km²

5.3 million people live in Scotland of which **1.5 million** live in just **4 cities**

466,000 people live in the Highlands & Islands – that's **8.8%** of the population living in half the country

POPULATION DENSITIES

66 / km²
Scotland

11 / km²
Highlands & Islands

116 / km²
EU Average

LAND OWNERSHIP

85% private

12% public

3% enviromental organisations

50% of Scotland's land area is owned by less than **500** people

1,500 lichens

12,000 fungi species

1,000 mosses & liverworts

50,000 invertebrates

2,000 flowering plants

LAND USE

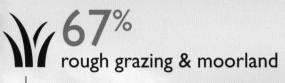
67%
rough grazing & moorland

12.5% of Scotland managed for grouse shooting

14.5% of Scotland managed for deer stalking
400,00 red deer

6 million sheep in Scotland

19%
total woodland cover

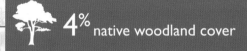
4% native woodland cover

37% average woodland cover across Europe

8% crops

2% urban

NATURE

2
National Parks

43
National Nature Reserves

396
Natura 2000 sites

79 bird species, such as golden eagle and capercaillie protected within Special Protection Areas

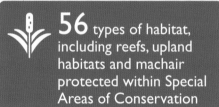
56 types of habitat, including reefs, upland habitats and machair protected within Special Areas of Conservation

1423
Sites of Special Scientific Interest

GONE

aurochs
crane
wolf
bear
wild boar
bittern
lynx
elk

3,700 pine martens

8,000 otters

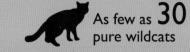
As few as **30** pure wildcats

Over **200** nesting pairs of osprey

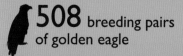
508 breeding pairs of golden eagle

WILD WORDS

by Sir John Lister-Kaye

Sir John Lister-Kaye is one of Scotland's best-known naturalists and conservationists. In 1986 he won the World Wilderness Foundation's gold award for environmental education and in 2003 he was awarded an OBE for services to nature conservation. He lives at Aigas, near Beauly.

When I came to live in Strathglass in the Highlands in 1969, each spring the glens around my home echoed with the bubbling calls of curlew. The rough pastures along the river flashed with gyrating, mewing lapwings staking out their tussocky nesting grounds. High above the woods redshank, greenshank, golden plover and dunlin nested. In the pinewoods I could always put up a capercaillie or a trio of black grouse, which would wing away into the forest.

Not so now. The capercaillie have all gone and the black grouse are a rare sight. The sound of curlews is missing and I have to drive several miles to find the nearest nesting lapwings. Gone, too, are the blue mountain hares from these parts, and the wigeon that used to nest on the rushy river flats. But there are many thousands of red deer compounding decades of overgrazing by hill sheep - so many deer, in fact, that I am forced to conclude that we have been getting things badly wrong for a long time.

It has taken an unconscionable time for the degradation of the Highland hills to become widely understood by land managers. Or is it perhaps that the romance of the great Highland Victorian sporting era was simply too powerful and captivating, blinkering owner and agent alike? For a hundred years it was a marketing success founded upon an exclusive opportunity, but it is one which has been badly managed and has failed to sustain its reputation.

Ten thousand years ago man arrived to find a pristine wilderness of rich climax vegetation: Scots pine, sessile oak and downy birch, willow, hazel and alder, rowan and gean, with a patchwork of heather clearings and slopes, mountain grasslands and sphagnum-rich bogs, with arctic-alpine scrub rising to the moss and tundra-lichen summits. There were some five million acres of upland through which reindeer, red and roe deer, wild ox, brown bear, wolves, lynx, beaver, and wild boar roamed, each according to its ecological niche, side by side with the familiar remnant wildlife we know today.

As farming developed there were gradually more and more people and fewer and smaller forests for what was left of the native wildlife. Fertility had arisen from the bountiful legacy of ten thousand years of forest soils accumulated since the end of the last ice age. But there were too many people with too many grazing animals for such a hostile climate and such a ponderous natural restoration process. The native pine forests and birch and oak woods, those key soil-creating ecosystems, were seriously depleted; the incisor teeth of grazing and browsing animals preventing regeneration and halting nature's restoration cycle in its tracks. Soon the Highlander was pinned to subsistence.

Spent was the forest legacy and scarce was its game and the life of Highlanders became unremitting toil. But Highland lairds were short of cash and global markets were opening up for goods and commodities like wool and timber. Many of the few remaining oak and pine forests were sold, felled and converted into charcoal to fuel the blast furnaces of the new industrial era. Then huge flocks of Cheviot sheep were driven north from the Southern Uplands to exploit the hill grazings. Vast tracts of upland were taken in hand and the new style of Highland estate had been created for the benefit of sheep.

When the price of wool collapsed, grazing pressure was dramatically reduced. Heather flourished and an accidental ecological niche was created in favour of the red grouse. Gradually, from the end of the 18th century, the Highland sporting tradition began to develop and expand. In 1842 the young Queen Victoria and Prince Albert discovered the Highlands. Hunting the red deer was the traditional sport of chiefs and kings. Salmon fishing was exhilarating in those tumbling, boulder-strewn rivers. Now there was a glut of grouse exploding across the predator-free moors, which were daily combed by tweed-clad gamekeepers with shotguns, traps and poisons. By 1850 wealthy folk would pay huge sums for their prestigious sport, which encouraged the building of new roads, houses and lodges.

An extract from the Topographical, Statistical and Historical Gazetteer of Scotland for the year 1853 is a gripping insight into what was really happening on the ground:

'Glengarry...was sold in 1840 to Lord Ward for £91,000 (over £3 million today). It abounds in game...but, like most estates...it has also been subject to the ravages of vermin... ...this gentleman...engaged numerous gamekeepers... awarding prizes of £3 to £5 to each of those who should prove the most successful...The keepers pursued the slaughter with undeviating rigour and attention. The result has been the destruction, within the last three years of above 4,000 head of vermin, and a proportional increase in the stock of game.'

The editor of the Inverness Courier of the day was struck by this report.

'We were anxious to learn the extent...of the vermin destroyed...To such of our readers as are fond of natural history, the list will prove interesting; the following list of vermin destroyed at Glengarry, from Whitsunday 1837 to Whitsunday 1840:- 11 Foxes; 108 Wildcats; 246 Martin cats; 106 Polecats; 301 Stoats and Weasels; 67 Badgers; 48 Otters; 78 House cats going wild; 27 White-tailed Sea-eagles; 15 Golden eagles; 18 Osprey or Fishing-eagles; 98 Blue hawks or Peregrine falcons; 7 Orange-legged falcons; 11 Hobby hawks; 275 kites, commonly called Salmon-tailed Gledes; 5 Marsh-harriers or Yellow-legged hawks; 63 Goshawks; 285 Common buzzards; 371 Rough-legged buzzards; 3 Honey buzzards; 462 Kestrels or Red-hawks; 78 Merlin hawks; 83 Hen-harriers or Ring-tailed hawks; 6 Jer-falcon or Toe-feathered hawks; 9 Ash-coloured hawks or Long blue-tailed hawks; 1,431 Hooded or Carrion crows; 475 Ravens; 35 Horned owls; 71 Common fern-owls; 3 Golden owls; and 3 Magpies.'

In his 1990 Raleigh Lecture, Professor Christopher Smout, Scotland's Historiographer Royal, describes this purge of wildlife as 'a major modification of the natural world.' He cites further evidence of the systematic elimination of birds of prey and mammal predators at this time '...on the Sutherland estates of Langwell and Sandside, 295 eagles were destroyed between 1819 and 1826...and 600 polecat skins brought to the Dumfries fur market in a year in the 1830s.'

All estates held a fervent commitment to the extermination of all predatory wildlife. The important conclusion Professor Smout draws is that: 'the volume of prey species in the Highlands - voles, mice, hares, small birds and so on...clearly no longer exist at anything like the densities necessary to support such numbers of predators, presumably because of damage done to their habitat by two centuries of modern land-use.' The evidence is stark. Clear-felled and overgrazed uplands cannot support wildlife. As a consequence, vast tracts of upland moor and mountain are now virtually empty.

By the mid-19th century an unstoppable red deer fashion had been born and endorsed by the royals, now known as the Balmorality Epoch. By 1912 the number of sporting estates had grown to more than two hundred and over 3.6 million acres were exclusively dedicated to sport. So romantic was the idyll that no one noticed that it was also exclusively extractive. The grazing pressure of greatly increased deer herds and range were compounding the earlier catastrophic extractions of timber and sheep overgrazing while absolutely nothing was being put back into the exhausted soils.

The legacy we live with today is a sorrier tale, which appears to have escalated faster in my lifetime than in the whole of recorded history. The grouse vanished from 70% of their range at the beginning of the 20th century. The Atlantic salmon is in serious decline in almost every Highland river, and the red deer, the fox and the hoodie crow have exploited ecological niches unintentionally provided by a compilation of land-use systems introduced by governments, which have often rebounded tragically upon the land and its wildlife.

Between 1960 and 2000 the red deer population has rocketed from around 150,000 animals to 500,000, with anything up to another 200,000 uncounted; including roe and sika deer in commercial forestry plantations encouraged by grants and tax incentives. Hundreds of thousands of acres of fenced conifers sprang up, forcing deer to new areas where increased grazing pressure further damaged their habitat and that of other wildlife. Trees grew thick and fast, but not before high rainfall had scoured the furrows and carried fine silt into the burns and spawning redds, injuring the river system into the bargain.

So where are we today? The reasons for the reduction of wildlife like curlew, lapwing, golden plover and greenshank, as well as game birds like capercaillie and black grouse, are superficially very simple. If natural ecosystems can be restored, most of the species concerned will eventually return of their own accord. After forty-five years of living in the midst of sporting estates, it is clear to me that we urgently need to develop a sustainable land ethic based upon fundamental ecological principles. One that permits nature to replenish the exhausted habitats upon which the whole sporting economy is founded: an ethic which becomes an accepted part of the sporting tradition. It has to be universally understood that you cannot have your sport without signing up to a regular, continuing cycle of restoration.

A pair of curlew fly up river in the spring, returning to where they had hatched, to find a suitable ground-nesting site. Four young hatch and are flightless for another six weeks. The parent birds begin the slow trek downhill to wetland. The chicks range about feeding themselves on insects and bugs. It is a hazardous journey. Herons, gulls, adders, weasels, foxes, crows will all have a go at a curlew chick. But the habitat has been grazed to a fraction of its natural height with a much-reduced variety of bugs for the chicks to eat. When the predator strikes, there is nowhere to hide. The chicks scatter - and are picked off one by one. Eventually there will be no curlews returning to that glen to breed. But that is not the end of the lament.

Rain falling in the hills should filter slowly through bog, scrub and woodland to emerge into the marshes, lochs and river systems as a nutritious soup literally feeding the whole freshwater ecosystem. It is what young trout and salmon depend upon, and ultimately, everything else downstream: the otter, the kingfisher, the dipper, the mallard and the teal. But if you burn and overgraze the hills, not only does that rain run off much faster, carrying peat and silt with it, but it also collects far less life-giving nutrition to hand out on its way through the system. Lochs fill with dark, acid water inimical to fish and aquatic life, and the rivers and burns flash-flood,

further flushing out and eroding the system. We should not be surprised that salmon are in trouble.

So how do we tackle this depressing problem? Ownership and usage change all the time, but the Land Agency profession is a continuum of professional expertise which has a real opportunity to influence and develop an ethic. I believe it is the duty of land agents to make it clear to sporting estates that with ownership comes a mandatory responsibility for natural restoration.

Secondly, we need to address deer numbers urgently and permanently. Until ecological principles are universally applied, we are only tinkering with the problem. A land ethic needs to require all sporting estate owners to sign up to a dedicated programme of natural restoration based on sound ecology. This would be 'seeing the big picture' - a process of giving back to nature now widely known as 'rewilding' - at the same time as planning and developing habitat for the game species and other wildlife upon which the sporting tradition depends. A future generation of sportsmen would once again be able to echo Prince Albert's sentiments: 'The country is really very beautiful, although severe and grand, perfect for sports of all kinds.'

SCOTLAND
A REWILDING JOURNEY

Written by

Susan Wright, Peter Cairns and Nick Underdown

Images by

Peter Cairns | Mark Hamblin | James Shooter | Richard Shucksmith | Philip Price
Guy Richardson | Laurent Geslin | Ronan Dugan | Aidan Maccormick

The big picture

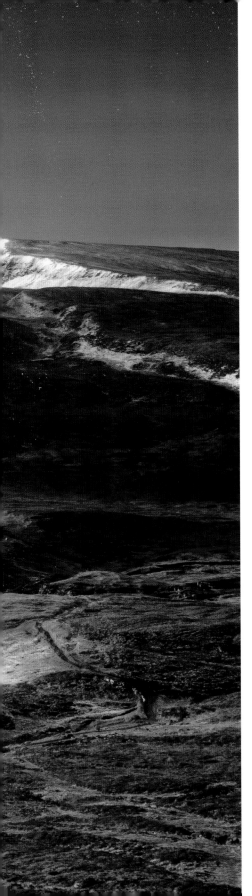

S cotland's sweeping mountain vistas are as spectacular as any in the world. Hewn from rock that spewed from lava millions of years ago, our peaks and ridges are dramatic and untamed. They offer breath-taking views, life-changing experiences for the explorer, and thrilling challenges for the hard-core adventurer. Solid and dependable, resistant to being chopped down or made extinct, they define our landscapes. It's no surprise there are over 40 words in Gaelic for a hill - from the mightiest *beinns* through the *sgùrrs* to the *mealls* and the small rounded *cnocs*. Scotland is a land of incredible shape and form.

This is especially true in the Highlands. Assynt would be less without Suilven and Stac Pollaidh. Stirling would be diminished without the distant presence of Ben Ledi sitting on the Highland edge. The Cairngorms would not be a national park were it not for the mountain massif at its core. And Skye is famous the world over for the Cuillin mountains and the Quiraing, a unique geological feature that dominates the northern end of the Trotternish Ridge.

Thousands come to Scotland every year to revel in such awe-inspiring landscapes. It's easy to be seduced by these perceived symbols of wild nature. But these geological wonders, such as the Quiraing, are surrounded mostly by ecological deserts; land that has lost its natural woodlands and complex vegetation communities and therefore, the many species that would once have thrived there. These are the species that fuelled the natural processes that govern the wild - predation, scavenging, decay and regeneration - the processes that drive every healthy living system on Earth.

It is said that a red squirrel could once travel from Lockerbie to Lochinver without ever touching the ground. This hasn't been possible for centuries. Scotland's native woodlands have been dismantled into tiny, fragmented islands, which now cover just 4% of Scotland's land mass. These islands imprison species such as red squirrels, crested tits and capercaillie that are unable to cross large areas of open ground. That open ground has become Scotland's signature landscape, not only crafted by weather and geology over an unfathomable timescale, but dramatically altered by a manmade storm of fire, felling and over-grazing, executed in a comparative blink of the eye. Beautiful craggy snow-capped peaks dominate the photograph on the cover of this book, but notice the hinterland almost devoid of trees and shrubbery. When we really look at the Scottish landscape we start to see a history of ecological wounds.

It is said that a red squirrel could once travel from Lockerbie to Lochinver without ever touching the ground.

These patchwork moorlands, intensively managed to optimise red grouse numbers for shooting, cover an estimated 2.5million acres of Scotland's uplands.

In geological time our impact on the land can be measured in just a few seconds. Yet in those seconds we have radically changed the landscape, and our perception of it. Over the last 250 years, we've seen a huge intensification of pressures on the land. Devastated boggy grassland and treeless moors stretching beyond the horizon has become our dominant land type. Centuries of sheep and deer grazing have reduced our uplands to shadows of the vibrant, species-rich landscapes they could be. We've lost all of our large carnivores and most of our large herbivores. Cultivation of land for grouse and angular monoculture plantations of exotic conifers have further reduced biodiversity and we now stand as one of the most nature-depleted nations on Earth. Against this backdrop of ecological decline, it's little surprise that our landscapes support far fewer people than they once did.

Yet all can seem well. Nature is still around us - from the bees in our gardens and the oak trees in the park to the buzzard mewing over hill and field, or the deer that bolts across the golf course. For those who want to delve more deeply, we can strike out for many a beauty spot and breathe in the great Scottish outdoors. We can visit one of our many fantastic nature reserves. Created over the last 60 years to protect fragments of life that we recognise as special, each one is a treasure trove of fascinating wildlife and notable geography - from otters to red squirrels, ancient pine trees to blanket bog, puffins to whooper swans, and grasslands to shifting sands. They're rich sources of pleasure, places we can visit to get closer to nature. They're a glimpse of what was once the norm.

In the UK crested tits are confined to the pine forests of northern Scotland. The lack of woodland corridors allowing them to move freely between one forest fragment and another, effectively imprisons them within a limited range.

We have wildlife that's nationally and internationally important. Puffins, seals and basking sharks are all of significant conservation value in Scotland. We have species rebounding from centuries of decline or even extinction. Ospreys, beavers, sea eagles and pine martens are all making a comeback. We have amazing patches of Caledonian pinewood and rich remnants of Celtic rainforest that thrum with life. When all this good stuff is set against Scotland's stunning backdrop of brooding hills, dramatic ever-shifting light, some of the best cloud action in the world and the four seasons in half an hour phenomenon, there's no better place to be. But we cannot ignore that we're lacking something quite profound - nature working in its own way on a large scale. It is hugely fragmented and diminished; saving odd bits of it is not enough.

Doug Chadwick, a renowned American wildlife biologist sums it up perfectly: "The essence of nature is wholeness - a wholeness woven from infinite complexity. Trying to save it piece by piece doesn't really make much sense even if we had all the time in the world, and we most certainly do not."

Around 10% of the global Atlantic puffin population breeds around the British coastline.

In Scotland, the wholeness that Chadwick refers to is broken, unravelled by centuries of use and misuse. The intricate and balanced ecosystem that emerged from the ice has been chopped into a thousand little pieces. Our patchwork landscape is manifest of this. Small pockets of natural woodland exist in isolation from each other, restricting the movement of the wildlife that lives in them. Chunks of commercial conifer plantations are scattered as though determined by rolls of the dice. Roads that need no permission to be built carve up hillsides. Charred squares of heather sear the skyline.

None of this has been done to any grand design. People have just been getting on with it for hundreds of years, and over the last fifty or so, we've been trying to save nature piece by piece - a rare bird or insect here, a fragment of habitat there. But we face a desperate situation now that challenges our survival as human beings. Climate change and crashing biodiversity are critical threats. Yet we still seem unable to take actions that acknowledge we're bound up in an intricate web of life that ties us to the weather, the atmosphere, the seas, the soil, the animals, the birds, the insects, the flowers, the trees, the freshwater lochs and rivers. We opt first for short-term economic gain and second for technological solutions that ignore nature as our greatest ally.

Want to stop flooding downstream? Get a beaver to build a dam. Need a back-up? Plant some native trees on the hills to absorb the rainfall. Need a renewable fuel source? Plant more trees. Prevent damaging landslips? Trees offer a natural solution, along with montane shrubs higher up the hill that bind the loose soil together. Purify that filthy water? Send it through some reed beds or peatland. Want some aspirin? Grow some willow. Absorb excess carbon dioxide? Plant more native forests and restore more peatlands. Wondering how to reduce deer numbers effectively? Call on the lynx and the wolf. Feeling a bit gloomy? Go walk among the baby Scots pines in a regenerating pinewood. And on it goes. Nature giving. Nature doing what it does.

Naturally regenerating Scots pines, Abernethy Forest, Cairngorms.

It's time to really grasp all of this, to read and understand the landscape, its history and the crossroads at which we're standing. Most of us aren't ecologists. Most of us don't look at nature closely. If we were, if we did, we would better understand what has happened at the Quiraing and across huge areas of the Scottish uplands. We would better understand the conservationist Aldo Leopold when he wrote:

"One of the penalties of an ecological education is that one lives alone in a world of wounds. Much of the damage inflicted on land is quite invisible to laymen. An ecologist must either harden his shell and make believe that the consequences of science are none of his business, or he must be the doctor who sees the marks of death in a community that believes itself well and does not want to be told otherwise."

We can no longer bury our heads and assume all is well. Nature is in serious decline where it should be abundant. Without abundance, we can't achieve resilience. It's no good having species teetering on the edge of survival, doing just okay, or living in isolated fragments of habitat. They need to flourish. We need more than fragments, more than just small reservoirs of life. We need widespread naturally functioning forests of trees, flowers, fungi, insects, birds and mammals. We need to protect and restore our blanket bogs and wetlands. We need to bring back wildflower meadows and ensure healthy rivers. We need wholeness. We need nature. We need rewilding.

Predation and scavenging is a natural process benefiting not only top predators like golden eagles, but a wide range of others birds, mammals and insects. The carcass of this red deer hind will eventually be absorbed back into the soil, providing nutrients for fresh plant growth.

Rewilding is not about recreating some random point in history or developing a natural world theme park. Neither is it about getting rid of people and replacing them with nature. Rewilding is the large-scale restoration of naturally functioning ecosystems on land and at sea. This means allowing nature to do its own thing and establish natural processes - such as predator-prey dynamics and carcass scavenging.

Rewilding is about connectivity across the landscape, encouraging native woodland to expand and give animals freedom to roam. In expanding woodland, red squirrels may move from tree to tree and black grouse can feed in boggy clearings.

Rewilding is about allowing rivers lined by alder and willow to meander as they want and allowing natural debris to create pools for salmon and trout while enriching the water for insects and bird life.

Rewilding is about restoring - rewetting - Scotland's water-purifying, carbon-storing peatlands that have been drained and burned across huge areas.

Rewilding is about allowing complex natural vegetation communities to grow, live and die creating deadwood for fungi, insects, woodpeckers and treecreepers.

Rewilding is understanding that a forest, a wetland, a peatland or a river is less of a physical entity and more a set of dynamic processes with no pre-determined end point.

At its most basic level, rewilding expands and joins up bits of nature rather than fragmenting them further, resulting in more wildlife, not less. Rewilding contributes to that all-important wholeness.

A key element of rewilding is connectivity across the landscape, allowing animals freedom to roam. This expanding native pine forest in Rothiemurchus in the Cairngorms, will benefit capercaillie, wildcats, pine martens and wood ants.

To do this we need to think big, beyond our smattering of nature reserves. We need huge bundles of imagination to envisage what the future can look like for Scotland, especially in our ecologically denuded uplands. And we need the geographical scale that can rebuild ecosystems for the future. This isn't about trying to control nature; it's about working with nature. Rewilding shouldn't be seen as a threat. Scotland itself - the Highlands in particular - is perfectly placed to become a world leader in ecosystem repair and restoration. For most of our history we've lived alongside an abundance of wildlife and we can do so again. A healthy, prosperous future is possible for the land and for us. We are, in fact, inextricably linked.

"Rewilding and re-peopling are not incompatible," says Professor James Hunter, historian and long-standing advocate of land reform. Indeed, this is being demonstrated across Europe where iconic wildlife species, such as lynx, wolves and bears, are coming back and people in rural areas are finding ways to live and prosper alongside them. In places like the Coa Valley in Portugal, the Apennines in Italy and the Carpathians in Romania, local people are pushing rewilding actions to improve the places they live in and to provide new economic opportunities. There are early signs of a changing philosophy here in Scotland – in parts of the Cairngorms,

Torridon, Assynt, Affric and the Borders. Pioneering initiatives are underway to restore degraded landscapes and to make the ecological, economic and social case for a wilder Scotland.

We need to be bolder. It took the best part of 20 years of campaigning and paperwork to reintroduce beavers. Consider that against a worldwide picture that has seen the number of wild animals living on the planet halve since 1970. The latest State of Nature report ranks Britain 189 out of 218 countries evaluated for their 'biodiversity intactness'. In just half a century, 50% of our species have declined and 15% are at risk of disappearing altogether. Here in Scotland that includes the Scottish wildcat and the capercaillie.

We're one of the wealthiest countries in the world. We can surely do better. It's time to recognise our obligations as a socially and environmentally responsible nation, and to see that a healthier and wealthier Scotland go hand in hand. It's time for action.

So this book is a plea to help nature - not the fragments and threads, but the whole. And in doing so, to help people. Having a vision for a wilder Scotland is having a vision for our own well-being into the future. Wild is not about the places where people are absent. The true wild is where natural processes flourish, where ecosystems are working in all their colourful complexity to give life to the land and everything on it, including us. That's our vision for a wilder Scotland. That's the big picture.

> "The essence of nature is wholeness - a wholeness woven from infinite complexity. Trying to save it piece by piece doesn't really make much sense even if we had all the time in the world, and we most certainly do not.
>
> *Doug Chadwick, Wildlife Biologist*"

Forest restoration efforts in Glen Affric started 60 years ago. Today, this rich mosaic of woodland, wetland and moorland serves as an example of what could be created across much larger areas of Scotland.

Trees are life

For billions of years, life on Earth has been evolving. From ocean-dwelling single cell organisms, a diverse and complex array of life found its way onto land and then into the air, forming a biosphere containing millions of interdependent species. The countless ecological relationships that formed between these species helped to maintain environmental conditions such as temperature and rainfall, the very conditions that human life now depends upon.

Pine trees are relative newcomers to the biosphere, dating back just a few million years. A single Scots pine might live for 700 years and during its lifetime will provide food and shelter for a mind-boggling community of living organisms. Even in death its skeletal frame, worn and withered over centuries, will continue to give sustenance to animal hitchhikers and dependent neighbours.

Cutting down a single pine tree might not seem significant, but in doing so, we arrest its contribution to a wider community of unimaginable lifeforms. Cutting down or burning whole forests, as we have done across endless miles, unravels millions of years of evolutionary history. Planting replacement trees is a poor substitute, because a forest is much more than just trees.

When Scotland emerged from the last Ice Age 10,000 years ago, life slowly took hold. Mosses and lichens clung on to bare rock, plants reached into shallow glacial soils and in time, trees took root. Birch, rowan and aspen led the way, followed by Scots pine, oak, ash, yew, holly and the full gamut of what we now call native trees. The notion of forest and not forest would have been irrelevant in these days before agriculture. The land just was - a mix of trees, meadows, peatlands, wetlands, rivers, grasses, waterfalls, lochs and mountains. As the landscape became rich in vegetation, all manner of animals found a home. Most of them, including boar, beavers, wolves and lynx, would be a part of Scotland until long after the arrival of the Romans in 1AD. By this time, however, we had already lost an estimated half of our woodlands.

Rewilding is not just about bringing trees back, but here in Scotland it's a good place to start. Our woodland cover presently stands at around 19%, much of this comprising exotic conifer plantations, which support comparatively little life. Compare this with a European Union average of 40% and it's easy to see that trees are a key component of our ecological deficit.

Trees are incredible givers of good things such as fresh air, food, and shelter against rain, sun and wind. Dead and alive they're a home and food source for innumerable plants, animals and insects. They suck up vast quantities of water, which helps to prevent flooding and dries out boggy land. They put nutrients into soils and rivers through their roots and decomposing leaves. On their own, they have different qualities for fire and timber, and offer many medicinal uses. Willow trees contain the ingredients for aspirin, while chemicals found in the yew tree are made into a chemotherapy drug to fight cancer. You can purify water by passing it through pine needles and turn oak leaves into wine. But when trees get together as forests, the real magic happens.

Trees work with each other – and with the fungi, plants, insects, birds and animals around them - to form a powerful life force. This is the natural forest, a dynamic and complex ecosystem, and the cornerstone of our existence. Forests give us vast amounts of oxygen that we need to breathe, they regulate our climate and remove carbon dioxide and other pollutants from the atmosphere.

A forest is much more than a sea of trees. A complex community of soil microbes, lichens, mosses, shrubs, tiny trees, huge trees, dying and dead trees, come together as a constantly evolving system.

Monoculture plantations don't perform quite the same trick. They're important as a timber crop but they support much less wildlife and contribute less to our planet's life-supporting biosphere. A clue as to why this is the case can be found when you try to walk through them. The trees are often planted in a regimented fashion, close together with little light reaching the forest floor, and not much surrounding vegetation. They will usually be felled in large chunks every 25 years and replanted. In an ecological timeframe commercial forests are here today, gone tomorrow, along with any wildlife in them.

In Scotland, one impact of commercial forestry plantations with their jarring straight edges has been psychological. People see tightly packed squares of Sitka spruce, so unwelcoming to walkers, and recoil at the thought of having more trees on the hills. But these cash crops are not our natural woodlands. Scotland's natural woodlands contain a rich mix of plants and animals, and they store more carbon. The loss of such woodlands and forests on a global scale is accelerating climate change and decimating wildlife. Cutting down forests creates carbon emissions, while new conifer plantations absorb less than the deciduous forests they replace. A report in the journal Nature states that:

'From 1750 to 1850, roughly 190,000 square kilometres of Europe's forest were cut down for fuel and to clear land for agriculture.

Forests have since rebounded on an area more than twice that size, but fast-growing conifers have replaced deciduous trees across roughly 633,000 square kilometres. Although European forests continue to take up carbon, the shift in composition means that they now hold 3.1 billion tonnes less than they did in 1750.'

In Scotland, we've almost completed the process of replacing our native broadleaf woodlands with non-native plantations. We're contributing to deforestation around the world because we have to import the vast majority of our timber and wood products. This presents us with a challenge because it's not enough to simply plant more trees, although that's needed too. We need to work to expand our native woodlands, to give them the space and the conditions to regenerate, heal and grow.

Currently the opposite is happening. Around half of our native woodlands are in unfavourable condition. In a healthy wood there will be trees of all ages - the gnarled oldies, the steadfast adults, more spritely teenagers, younger saplings, and, just popping out of the woodland floor, the baby seedlings. Many of our woods are full of old trees but the youngsters are missing. Or there are saplings that can't get past knee height because excessive numbers of deer are nibbling them. If trees can't grow to maturity and replace the older trees as they die off, then whole woodlands, and all the life they support, disappear.

Tightly packed conifer plantations are important for timber production, but are less biodiverse than natural woodlands comprising a wide mix of species.

Woodland ecosystems are intricate affairs. Beneath the leaf litter, which lies on the woodland floor, trees and plants speak to each other using a complex language of chemical signals. They share nutrients through the mycelium on their roots. Mycelia are microscopic threads of fungi that grow out from these roots to form a vast network underground - the wood wide web. The fungi helps trees and plants to suck up water, as well as nutrients from the soil such as nitrogen and phosphorous. The tree sends carbohydrates down to the fungi in return. But the wider network enables this quid pro quo action to take place between different trees and plants across a large geographical area. If a seedling isn't getting enough light, a neighbouring tree might send over carbon through the network. A dead tree will continue to receive nutrients from its surrounding tree family.

We can catch glimpses of these amazing woodland habitats in the remnants of rainforest found on our wetter western fringes and in the pockets of ancient pinewoods scattered across the country. The pinewoods on the islands of Loch Maree in Wester Ross are a great example. A diverse woodland structure has managed to survive here, which includes not only pines but bog woodland, alder carr, blanket bog and the rare rock whitebeam tree. Otters, black-throated divers, sea eagles and myriad dragonflies prosper on the back of these complex plant communities. These wooded oases demonstrate a richness of life that's possible across much of Scotland - a sign of what grew out of the ice and what can grow again.

Loch Maree, Wester Ross.

Black darter, Wester Ross.

Black-throated diver, Loch Maree, Wester Ross.

Across the water from the Loch Maree islands, sitting a few vertical miles below the summit of Slioch, is a surviving strip of Coastal Temperate Rainforest, the Letterewe Oakwoods. This type of rainforest, also found in the northwest United States, Japan and Australia, is characterised by high annual rainfall, so it's little surprise to discover it's a feature of the British Isles. The remaining rainforest on Loch Maree has managed to rebound from periods of intense felling over several centuries. Today it boasts oak trees that have stood for 200 years and a mix of birch, rowan, holly, ash, alder and pine. Similar remnants can be found around Loch Sunart on the Ardnamurchan peninsula, the Ardvar woodlands in Assynt, and Taynish on the west coast. They're the visible remains of a precious ecosystem that once thrived and could thrive again if we can relieve the surrounding land of intense grazing pressure.

The Loch Maree oakwoods and pine forest have adapted over 8,000 years to thrive in the cold, wet conditions typical of the east Atlantic seaboard. This contrasts with the drier cold snaps and warmer summer blasts that frequent the inland pinewoods of the Cairngorms, where the forests of Abernethy and Rothiemurchus are very different, but no less rich in life. Our native vegetation is amazingly versatile. Nature will try its hardest to plant trees anywhere it can, but minerals in the soil, rainfall levels, temperature and invisible pathogens all determine what grows where. One thing is certain: when people state that trees cannot grow in the harsh environs of the Scottish Highlands, our surviving fragments of woodland tell us otherwise. They may have suffered under the axe, and struggle with overgrazing, but they can handle lots of weather.

Sessile oak woodland dominates in the temperate rainforests of Scotland's west coast, like here at Taynish in Argyll.

Not everyone wants more trees. Some people fear Scotland's panoramas and classic views will be lost, or that an impenetrable jungle will grow and surround us. Natural woodland is just one part of rewilding and although the situation in Scotland is particularly desperate, rewilding doesn't set out a pre-determined level of tree cover; it's about giving nature the opportunity to determine this for itself. Across much of Scotland this is likely to result in a patchwork where woodland takes its place among bog, moorland and alpine habitats. We can help re-ignite that process by planting in areas where there is no local seed source, but in the main, rewilding recognises that nature knows best.

Nature works on a large scale, so giving it the space it needs for natural processes to establish themselves is something we need to embrace. The landscape will then be shaped on nature's terms, not ours. Rewilding need not happen everywhere. It's a choice of land use that can co-exist alongside farming, forestry and recreational activities. Some believe we don't have the space for such landscape-scale ambitions, but if you consider the upland area of Scotland currently managed for grouse shooting and deer stalking covers around 5 million acres - perhaps it's an easier choice than we think.

The regenerating alders and willows along this river channel will stabilise its shifting gravels and shade the water to the benefit of fish, which in turn benefits fish predators like ospreys.

Rewilding asks us to look beyond individual species or habitats and to think about relationships and processes that interlink and are part of the greater whole. The health of our wild salmon is linked to the health of the oceans, which affects the health of the rivers, which is linked to the health of the woodland through which they pass. This recurs time and again in nature. "When we try to pick out anything by itself, we find it hitched to everything else in the universe," wrote the Dunbar environmentalist John Muir, which were arguably the truest words he ever wrote.

The nutrient cycle between our rivers, lochs and woodlands is a great example of how nature has evolved. In a healthy ecosystem, falling leaves and other woodland debris will drop into the water and add nutrients that fuel a vast array of aquatic life, including migrating fish such as salmon and sea trout, which in turn carry nutrients from the ocean like nitrogen and phosphorous. These are good for the soil. When animals such as otters, ospreys or sea eagles (and bears where they exist), catch the salmon, they'll take it to eat onshore. The nutrients in the fish will pass into the soils from the fish carcass and through the animal's digestive droppings. This is nature's power in motion.

It can be witnessed in Alaska's Tongass Rainforest where it's said that the local bears are made of salmon and so too are the trees. "The salmon not only help grow the trees, they actually grow in the trees," points out Amy Gulick, author of Salmon in the Trees. "Once you understand this remarkable connection, you quickly see that everything is connected."

If we give space to nature and stand back, we can let these near limitless connections develop and form. And from it we may get woodlands, wild flower meadows, grasslands or wetlands from which countless species can flourish, including us. It's not about pines or wood ants or capercaillie or red squirrels, it's about complex communities being allowed to function as they need to; as we need them to. We can never accurately predict the outcomes of nature and neither should we try. We just need to believe in its ability to grow and adapt in ways that make sense naturally. It's had plenty of time to practice.

Rewilding asks us to look beyond individual species or habitats and to think about relationships and processes that interlink and are part of the greater whole.

by Dr Duncan Halley

Dr. Duncan Halley was born and educated in Scotland. In 1993 he travelled to Norway on a one year research contract. 25 years later, he is still there. He works for the Norwegian Institute for Nature Research on a variety of subjects including grazing ecology, landscape history, and restoration ecology. Work has included research in Norway, broadly in Europe, in Japan, and in southern Africa.

About ten years ago I hosted a group of Forestry Commission Scotland staff visiting my workplace. One day I took them to a site immediately above the rocky shoreline of the west coast, directly exposed to the open Atlantic. They explained to me three reasons why this place should be treeless: too windy, too salty and in the cool, wet climate, the hard, infertile geology was unable to support woodland soils.

Yet the site we were standing on was covered with rapidly regenerating, naturally seeded woodland; mainly birch and Scots pine, but also rowan, aspen, and bird cherry. Back then, most of this landscape would have been referred to as scrub; now most people call it open woodland.

I've left out one detail: the site I'm speaking of is in mid-Norway, 500km north of John O Groats. This place is as windy as anywhere on the west coast of Scotland, including the Western Isles. It's just as wet, and average temperatures are above zero all year – so no protective

effect of snow. The latitude means the sun provides less energy than it does in Scotland. All in all, this place is distinctly less favourable for tree growth than anywhere on the Scottish west coast.

The woodland is new, though. Almost all of the woodland up and down the Norwegian west coast is, from its southern tip opposite Dornoch to north of the Arctic Circle. Like the west Highlands, it has been a predominantly open landscape of moorland and rough grazing for millennia. Peat was the main fuel until the 1950s.

This can be hard to believe if you visit the region today. It's now heavily wooded, and peat has been entirely replaced by fuelwood. All the trees are young, and over large areas, are still visibly recolonising. The rate of woodland spread is simply staggering. Deciduous woodland, mainly birch, rowan, alder, aspen and bird cherry, all naturally regenerated, has more than doubled in volume over the last 20 years.

Coniferous woodland is up by more than half. West Norway is adding over 300 km2 of woodland a year just from natural spread. The extra annual carbon sink this represents comfortably exceeds the Scottish Government's target for 2020. All from natural regeneration, and 'for free'.

A few years after that first visit, I started getting questions from colleagues in Scotland asking why the land cover was so different. Initially, renewed claims were made that Norway's climate was very different from Scotland's and that the heavier winter snows explained the obvious difference in land cover.

Fortunately, weather statistics can easily and accurately be compared. In fact, southwest Norway - the provinces of Vest-Agder, Rogaland, and Hordaland - has very similar weather patterns to the Scottish Highlands. There's no lying snow on the coast most winters, and never very much or for very long in even the hardest years. This isn't surprising: these regions lie at the same latitudes as Dornoch to Hermaness, and squarely in the same prevailing airstreams that dominate the climate of Scotland.

Oddly, the response was not 'thanks, problem solved', but, 'actually, it's not the snow, it's the temperature and rainfall - Norway is more continental'. This is certainly news to the residents of Bergen, where it rains nearly four metres a year. Norway is as wet or wetter than the Highlands and seasonal temperatures are very similar. But then it wasn't that either; it was the wind. It's much windier in Scotland and that's why there are no trees. In fact, the southwest coast of Norway is windier than anywhere on the Scottish coast. Force 10 storms occur every year.

There seemed to be a powerful desire to find a factor that could be said to have made these modern landscapes so different. Apart from the obvious one, that is: the human use of the land. Research shows a striking similarity in the landscape history of southwest Norway and of the Highlands. People in the two regions developed agriculture and livestock herding at about the same times, acquiring new technologies from bronze and iron, improved ploughs and water-driven sawmills. In west coast regions of Norway, as in the west Highlands, the process of deforestation was essentially complete by the Bronze Age.

It continued inland for many more centuries, reaching maximum extent in both regions in the 19th century. Houses in both regions were made from sod, or with drystone cavity walls filled with sods. Driftwood for roof timbers was highly prized and carefully preserved. Peat was the fuel. None of this should be surprising. Similar people, solving the problems of making a living in very similar conditions, and with similar effects.

From the 18th century, however, land use patterns in the Highlands changed radically. Subsistence pastoralism was replaced by sheep ranching, and later that was partly replaced by recreational hunting for deer and grouse. The result was a maintained pressure on the landscape through grazing and muirburn. In southwest Norway the older pattern continued into the mid-19th century. Then, it began to break down, but in a very different way.

For centuries, southwest Norway had been a land of owner-occupied farms. The agent of change was mass voluntary emigration, mainly to the United States. Emigrants were mostly younger children of farmers and the landless - the people who tended the livestock.

Estimates are that about a third of the population left in the course of the next 40 years. The stream of emigration remained strong until the onset of the Great Depression in 1929.

As Norwegian farming operations consolidated on the most profitable areas, livestock numbers declined strongly, especially in the uplands. The first pulse of woodland regeneration in southwest Norway dates from this time, and research demonstrates the cause was the decline in grazing pressure.

Grazing pressure declined further from the 1950s, as other work became more available and was considered more attractive. Grazing reached a minimum in 1969, but has since increased mainly due to a significant rise in the population of deer species. In Norway (as in Scotland) deer were reduced to small, scattered populations during the subsistence pastoralism period. Their increase now means that in much of southwest Norway the number of red deer harvested per unit area is similar to that of red deer estates in Scotland.

The deer are 40% larger (and we know this is for nutritional, not genetic, reasons), so venison extracted is greater per unit area and trophy heads better. Deer densities, however, are much lower in Norway. Populations are maintained at optimal levels, and harvests are determined using modern game management science (large predators are absent from southwest Norway). Harvests are around 30% of the population each year, as compared to an average of 10% in Scotland.

The increase in Norway's deer numbers since 1969 has not prevented the natural rewooding of the landscape: it has never been faster than it is today. There is no biophysical reason why the same process could not occur in Highland Scotland, if grazing pressures were similarly reduced.

One of the most heartening developments of recent years has been the reappearance of significant natural regeneration onto deforested land in some parts of the Highlands. To those familiar with the pattern, it is very similar to the early stages of woodland re-establishment observed in Norway. I recently visited Glen Derry on NTS' Mar Lodge Estate. I had not seen it for about 25 years, and so my memory of the shaved ground under ageing pines was not faded by observing gradual change. The difference from the exuberant natural woodland regeneration and abundant, increasingly diverse ground layer of today was stark and impressive. It resulted from getting grazing pressures under control.

Greater biological productivity means greater economic productivity. There is more to extract and that extraction is more sustainable. Income streams in southwest Norway are more diverse than is currently usual in Scotland, where there is often a presumption that a piece of hill land must have a single dominating use - such as grouse, deer, sheep, timber, or conservation. Southwest Norway shows it does not have to be this way. A diverse range of sustainable land uses on the same piece of hill ground supports a population density outside the main towns of 18.4/km2, compared with 5.9/km2 in the Highland region. At the same time, it has a much more diverse flora and fauna and benefits from better flood buffering and fewer landslips.

Arguments that restoring Scotland's 'natural capital' is either impossible, or implies reductions in rural employment, both fail on the evidence. Kickstarting natural processes and therefore rural economies, would be the most prudent of investments. In the same climate and in the same geologies, Norway has proved it's not only possible but also hugely beneficial. Will Scotland follow suit?

Extensive woodland regeneration stretching up the slopes of Fidjadalen in southwest Norway, a region with similar geology and weather patterns to much of Highland Scotland.

Meet the neighbours

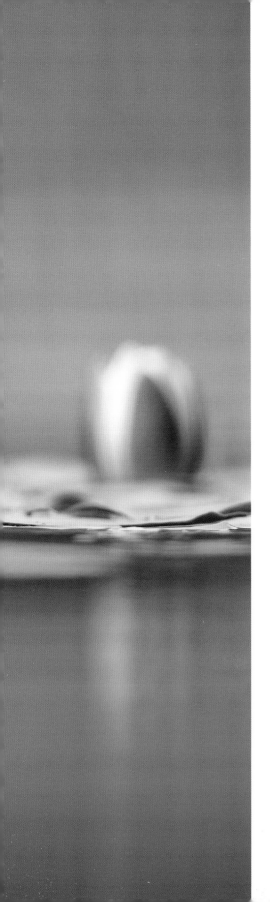

The beaver is back, making Scotland just a tiny bit wilder. This industrious rodent officially came home to Knapdale in Argyll in 2009 as part of a carefully considered reintroduction trial. Four beavers arrived from Norway, the first to glide across a Scottish loch since some time in the 1500s. Artificial lodges had been meticulously researched and constructed in preparation for their arrival, but when the beavers were released on one loch, they went into one end of their lodge and came right out the other never to return. It was nature at its finest. These beavers might not have known where they were but they knew what they had to do. They knew this manmade effort wasn't a place to call home so they built their own. That's the thing about nature, it just knows. It just does.

Scotland with its near-natural river systems and chains of freshwater lochs is perfect for beavers, yet the process of restoring them has been laboured and expensive. After decades of discussion, followed by five years of painstaking measuring and monitoring, the Scottish government has made the decision to allow the Knapdale beavers to stay. We are one of the last countries in Europe to do so. Austria, Belgium, Croatia, Czech Republic, Denmark, Estonia, Finland, France, Germany, Hungary, Italy, Latvia, Liechtenstein, Montenegro, the Netherlands, Poland, Romania, Serbia, Slovakia, Slovenia, Spain, Sweden and Ukraine have all brought beavers back. Most of these countries are much more crowded and industrialised than the Scottish Highlands. Germany now has 30,000 beavers, France 15,000.

Scotland's beaver population has been boosted by the parallel success of the 'illegal' beavers, which have now been given legal protected status, further east. They burst forth unofficially and without fanfare on the River Earn several years ago. From there they moved rapidly along to the Tay and its tributaries and have now reached as far as the North Sea to the east and Rannoch to the west. They've caused consternation by arriving without permission, but the beaver should never have left. Scotland was its home until people made them extinct, hunting them to profit from their pelts and their glandular oil.

We've lost many of our animal kingdom neighbours over the centuries, mostly at the hands of people. Wolves, lynx, bear, wild boar, cranes, kites, ospreys, goshawks and sea eagles have all gone extinct, and then some of them have returned. The osprey disappeared as a breeding bird for 40 years, the last one shot in 1916. Then one day in 1954, a single pair nested again at Boat of Garten in the Cairngorms. Now we have ospreys thriving in multiple locations across Scotland, each a draw for tourists and wildlife watchers.

Persecution and egg theft drove the sea eagle to extinction in 1918, before being reintroduced from Norway in the 1970s. Sea eagles now range across much of western and eastern Scotland. For most people they're a welcome success, but still only 100 pairs breed where there should be many hundreds more across the whole of the British Isles. The red kite, also made extinct through hunting and egg theft, was reintroduced in the late 1980s and 1990s and is slowly repopulating against a continuing backdrop of illegal persecution.

More recently the pine marten has bounded back. This was once Britain's second most common carnivore, but was pushed into the most remote pockets of the wooded Highlands. Now protected by law and expanding into new areas, this cat-sized stoat is playing an unexpected role in helping the red squirrel by predating the non-native grey - another example of nature ignoring our preconceptions and surprising us.

In recent decades pine martens have recolonised much of their former range and can now be seen on the edge of some of Scotland's busiest cities.

These successes should be celebrated. They show what can be done. Nevertheless, much of our wildlife is still in decline. Some species are finding it difficult to adapt to a rapidly changing climate and the challenges this brings. Pollution, pathogens, persecution and habitat fragmentation all continue to contribute to wildlife losses, but so too does a lack of scale and diversity. Nature needs scale. The places in Scotland where wildlife flourishes are small and isolated. A lack of diversity means that if one tree or plant species dies and there's nothing to take its place, the ecosystem falters. If an animal disappears or dies it will have a bigger impact where there are no others to fill the void.

Animals need natural corridors to give them freedom to roam, and help ensure genetic diversity as they come into contact with unrelated members of their own species. You can walk through Scotland's patches of native pinewood in less than a couple of hours and then stare out at mile after mile of treeless hillside. This lack of connectivity between one island of forest and the next prevents wildlife like red squirrels and crested tits from moving across the landscape. With physical isolation comes genetic stagnation, disease and the potential loss of a whole species.

Scottish wildcat caught on a camera trap in the Angus Glens.

This has been a big problem for the Scottish wildcat - our only surviving native species of cat, which is now spiralling towards the verge of extinction. The causes of the cat's demise are complex, and include persecution, but Perthshire-based ecologist Alan Ross, who has been studying this elusive creature for many years, points to habitat fragmentation as a key issue.

"The wildcat's dire plight is symptomatic of a Scottish landscape, which is as far removed from ecological equilibrium as it gets. Despite the pioneering work of conservation organisations and an increasing number of private landowners, Scotland's forests remain small and fragmented. If we are serious about saving wildcats - and many other species - we need to break away from what is presently a facile, sticking plaster approach to wildcat conservation and upland ecological restoration. We need to adopt a visionary and innovative approach to rewilding our degraded landscape if the wildcat is to be rescued from the brink of extinction.

I would like to see the creation of a Wildcat Forest Network, with patches of healthy habitat linked by designated wildcat corridors integrated into a national forest restoration initiative. In many cases, this could double up as part of a desperately needed flood mitigation scheme, incorporating natural resilience features from shelterbelts to beaver wetlands. It's simply inexcusable that Scotland is lagging behind the rest of the world in recognising the far-ranging socio-economic benefits of native forest restoration."

A lack of connectivity is what spurred Trees for Life to translocate red squirrels from Moray to ten areas of pinewood in the northwest Highlands. At the moment, it's the only way to get red squirrels back to these woods.

This wildlife overpass in Canada's Banff National Park provides a safe passage for animals moving from one part of their range to another. Such green corridors are now widespread across Europe, helping to mitigate the effects of habitat fragmentation as well as reducing traffic accidents.

Translocations and reintroductions are expensive and complicated, but they're vital for helping particular species and addressing specific problems. It's part of the bigger rewilding picture, which in the longer term is less about hands-on species management and more about creating the conditions for wildlife to thrive according to its own rules and rhythms. At present, the most connected habitats in Scotland's uplands are the habitats of ecological degradation - deer forest and grouse moor. If we can flip this, we can give nature the space it needs. This doesn't mean eliminating other land uses, but choosing to recognise the important role that wild nature plays in giving us life.

We saw an example of wild nature in action in the previous chapter, of how woodland helps salmon and salmon helps woodland. It's just one of the wondrous ways that wild nature enriches our soils. Insects and animals digest vegetation and deposit it as fertiliser back into the ground. Floods wash nutrients onto riverbanks to create fertile growing areas. Fires clear the way for new growth. And on it goes.

When nature is working fully, it follows a beautiful closed loop cycle of life. Every animal has a part to play, even those animals some of us don't like, never see or may never have heard of. Some animals have a bigger role than others. The beaver, for example, is a keystone species; meaning it has more far-reaching impacts than other species in the ecosystem. It's a water mechanic of supreme skill with powerful teeth and hands that work to fell trees, and gnaw on bark, to create ponds and wetlands that enable hundreds of other species to flourish. Their dams slow the flow of rivers, helping migrating fish and reducing flooding. When a beaver returns to a wetland, a whole host of aquatic and insect life comes back with it. Animal life in general experiences a surge. Rivers become less prone to flooding. Migrating fish are less likely to lose their spawning grounds, and trees benefit from the beaver's coppicing actions.

Red squirrels are absent from many forests where they once thrived. By moving small numbers from areas where they are abundant to squirrel-free forests, Trees for Life are creating new squirrel populations and in doing so, restoring the natural processes that red squirrels provide, such as the dispersal of tree seeds.

The wild boar, eradicated in Scotland in the 17th century, is another keystone species. It roots and snuffles on the woodland floor, breaking up vegetation and creating niches for tree and plant seeds. Badgers perform a similar function albeit on a smaller scale. So too the lynx, which preys on smaller roe deer, feeding itself and lots of scavengers at the same time. When the deer carcass rots and returns to the soil, it will help tree seedlings to grow. But the wolf, another native to Scotland, is one of the most profound shapers of landscape, as one of the more surprising recent YouTube sensations explains. In How Wolves Change Rivers, author George Monbiot spends four evocative minutes detailing the domino effect prompted by the reintroduction of wolves to Yellowstone National Park.

When nature is working fully, it follows a beautiful closed loop cycle of life. Every animal has a part to play.

Eurasian lynx feeding on roe deer, Switzerland. The ecological benefits provided by large carnivores such as lynx and wolves, are only just being fully understood.

He explains that the return of wolves caused the deer to graze for shorter times, and to move more often and avoid certain areas. This allowed a mix of tree species to regenerate, which attracted more birds and also increased the number of beavers. This prompted a surge of wildlife in beaver-made habitats, while the wolves' predation of coyotes helped rabbits and mice to flourish. These were tasty prey for raptors, weasels and foxes whose numbers then increased. The carcasses of wolf kills provided a food source for a wide range of animals, including bears. The bears also benefitted from more berries as the trees and plants returned. But the drama didn't end there. The rivers began to change, altering their flow and direction because as Monbiot concludes:

..."the regenerated forest stabilised the banks. They collapsed less often so that the rivers became more fixed in their course. By moving the deer around, the vegetation recovered on the valley sides so there was less soil erosion. So the wolves, small in number, transformed not just the ecosystem of Yellowstone National Park, this huge area of land, but also its physical geography."

It's a beautifully told story of the interdependencies in nature, of the numerous and vast interplays of living things where each species is following a natural cycle of life that connects to a bigger whole. This film made a star out of ecosystems with 40 million people viewing and sharing it widely on social media. The wolf, of course, was a charismatic lead actor. This top predator, loved and hated in equal measure, challenges us both physically and culturally. But as scientist L David Mech, who has spent a 57-year career observing and studying wolves in the United States says: "the wolf is neither a saint nor sinner except to those who make it so". It's simply an animal moving to its own natural rhythms and doing what it's meant to do.

The River Feshie in the Cairngorms has carved one of Scotland's best examples of a braided river system, with the turbulent waters washing huge amounts of gravel and silt one way and then another. Less than 300 years ago wolves would have hunted deer along this river.

If wolves could swim the English Channel they'd be here by now. They've been moving westwards over decades from Poland and Russia to take up residence in France, Germany, the Netherlands, Belgium and Denmark. Like the beaver, it should never have left. We remain one of the few countries in the world unwilling to live alongside apex predators, the primary obstacle being that we've simply grown used to life without them.

The wolf was finally made extinct in Scotland in the 1700s after centuries of persecution, which included being bounty for medieval kings who would pay a reward upon presentation of a wolf's tail. The wolf followed the disappearance of our other native carnivores. It is thought the lynx held on until around the Middle Ages. The brown bear probably survived until around the time of the Romans. We don't know for sure when the last one was killed, but there's evidence the Romans shipped Scottish bears to Rome for blood sports in their coliseums, hastening their demise.

The extinction of our wildlife speeded up in the late 18th and early 19th centuries when landowners started to establish sporting estates. They directed their gamekeepers to kill any animal deemed a threat to deer, grouse and the other game birds they wanted to shoot. The gun would radically alter the make-up of Scotland's wildlife, as John Lister-Kaye's example from Glengarry in 1853 alluded to in his Wild Words essay (see p12). It was a scale of destruction never seen before or since.

Today we are facing declining stocks of wild salmon. The wildcat teeters on the edge, as does the capercaillie. Our birds of prey still face widespread shooting, trapping and poisoning. Mountain hares are killed in their thousands on shooting estates with little knowledge of how sustainable this may be. In the absence of top predators, we try to mimic their actions by culling deer, but we do so according to our own arbitrary rules and not those found in nature. It is hardly surprising that our 'biodiversity intactness' ranks so poorly.

Scotland sits at the far northern edge of Europe, the only continent where predators are coming back in high numbers. Some are recolonising naturally, others are being reintroduced. Our continental cousins are learning to co-exist with these returning neighbours. In the Carpathians in Romania, where large herbivores have been hunted to the brink, bison are being reintroduced to take their place once again in the ecosystem, and in doing so benefiting countless other species. In the Coa Valley in Portugal, they've introduced the tauros, the back-bred genetic equivalent of the giant aurochs cow, to eat the excess vegetation that's causing wildfires every year. In the Velebit mountains in Croatia and the Rhodope mountains in Bulgaria, they're reintroducing more deer to increase grazing and open up the woodland canopy to improve biodiversity. In the Danube Delta in Ukraine they're bringing back wild konik horses to graze the rich vegetation that's returned with the re-flooding of land.

Highland cattle are used in some areas of Scotland to replicate the natural grazing patterns of long-lost large herbivores like aurochs. The selective grazing of Highlanders creates wet hollows, breaks up ground vegetation and aids the dispersal of tree seeds.

What are we going to do in Scotland to take our rightful place in this progressive, wilder Europe? It's not that we can't restore our missing species, it's that we won't. The beaver is back but will we allow it to expand across its full range? Can we help the sea eagle go from strength to strength? Can we do what's needed to save the wildcat and stop our salmon stocks declining? Can we open our hearts to that other feline, the lynx? And can we educate ourselves enough to have an intelligent and informed debate about the return of the wolf? These are important questions. Our life-support system is hanging in the balance and its good health relies on many things. Respecting and understanding the roles of all creatures is an essential step towards a future where we see ourselves not as separate from nature, but part of it.

We remain one of the few countries in the world unwilling to live alongside apex predators.

"Wetlands are tremendously important for biodiversity. They also serve to store water and improve its quality - they are the 'kidneys of the landscape'.
Professor Nigel Willby"

Sheep & shooting

In 1851 when celebrated artist Edwin Landseer depicted a royal stag against the majesty of the Highlands, he created an evocative and enduring image of Scotland's hills and glens, sealing a tradition in which wealthy Victorian industrialists came to the Highlands paying handsomely to shoot deer – particularly big trophy stags. The uniquely Scottish tradition of open hill stalking, or hunting, has changed little in almost two centuries and deer stalking remains at the cultural heart of many Highland communities. The treeless deer forests that cover around 2.8 million acres of Scotland's wildest country remain emblematic of a romantic period that many wish to retain.

Deer forests today dominate most maps of Scotland, especially north of the Central Belt. From the Forest of Reay in Sutherland through the Fisherfield and Letterewe Forests in Wester Ross to Rannoch; and then east to Balmoral and south to Alyth. These 'forests' are largely open hill areas with very few trees and hark back to the early origins of the word, which was used to denote land set aside for hunting.

Woodland would have been a feature of deer forests centuries ago, but today they are ecologically poor swathes of land. Walk into the hills beyond Slioch, for example. This is where the vast Kinlochewe, Letterewe and Fisherfield Forests meet. Walkers call this the last great wilderness, by which they mean remote, empty and hostile. Nature hasn't had much of a chance in this great sweep of land for centuries. You can see much the same when you reach the end of the pinewoods at Balmoral and set foot in the Balmoral Forest. Or where the Mar Lodge pinewood turns into the bare Forest of Mar. A similar scene is to be found as the stunning pines and birches of Glen Affric give way to the more lifeless Affric Forest. There are countless examples like these all over Scotland.

These bare uplands are the legacy of a shift that took place when Scotland's old cattle economy gave way to large scale, commercial sheep ranching. In the Borders, sheep rearing was a key activity as far back as the 13th century. The impacts on the majority of the hills are easy to see, where the slopes have been razed bare by centuries of intense grazing. In the Highlands, the sheep came later but the effects have been the same. Cows would have been a natural part of the landscape since the days of the aurochs, sustaining families and tribes in ancient times, fertilising the land with their dung and shaping woodlands through their grazing. Wildlife in this largely self-sustaining, low-impact pastoral economy was not untouched, but it was still plentiful.

Following the defeat of the Jacobites at Culloden in 1745, land ownership and land use altered dramatically, eventually culminating in the forced eviction of thousands of people from their homelands to make way for sheep. Highland landowners embraced the opportunity to make far more money than they ever could from their subsistence tenants. The Clearances caused severe hardship, and even death, for ordinary people and erased hundreds of settlements in the Highlands. They also sounded the death knell for a relatively low-impact way of life. Where cows had fed nutrients back into the hills, and grazed within limits, the new swarm of sheep nibbled incessantly. The heavy stocking sucked nutrients from the soils and gave nothing back, so when the soil lost its fertility and the markets shrunk, sheep farming went into decline.

When the sheep went, the people weren't allowed back. Instead, deer stalking and grouse shooting rapidly gained in popularity. Inspired by Queen Victoria and Prince Albert's purchase of Balmoral, the social elite from near and far snapped up land to turn into sporting estates. It started a pattern of land ownership that persists almost untouched today. These new estate owners worked hard to maximise deer numbers, shipping in animals from parks in England and elsewhere, and killing wildlife they considered vermin.

Most of Scotland's deer forests remain devoid of trees and shrubs, any chance of natural regeneration kept in check by high numbers of red deer.

Deer are browsing animals and at high densities they will overwhelm the vegetation and eat all regenerating saplings, leaving just older trees to die off one by one over time. With their natural predators long gone, deer have had plenty of time to proliferate. In 1959, when the Red Deer Commission was created, primarily to address damage to agriculture and forestry, Scotland's red deer numbers were estimated at around 150,000. Thirty years later that figure had doubled, and today, informed estimates hover around 400,000.

Such a high number of hungry mouths inevitably impacts on ground vegetation and emerging woodland. As the impact of over-grazing on the ecological health of the Highlands has become better understood, an ideological battle has evolved between traditional deer managers and those who lament the continuing demise of Scotland's native woodland. It has now taken the shape of a seemingly intractable cultural debate with trust and respect in short supply on both sides.

The 'deer problem' is nothing new. Acclaimed ecologist Frank Fraser Darling famously described the Highlands as a 'wet desert' and advised the Red Deer Commission that 60,000 might be an optimum population for red deer in Scotland. No fewer than seven government-appointed inquiries have sought to address the problem. Despite repeated calls for land managers and stalkers to radically reduce deer densities, the numbers in many areas remain stubbornly high.

There are good reasons for this. Traditional sporting estates are valued, in part at least, on the number of deer that can be shot on their land, and they work to grow and maintain high deer numbers so there are plenty available for well-paying clients to shoot.

The Stag Ballroom at Mar Lodge contains the antlers of over 2,000 red deer stags, a graphic symbol of a deep-rooted cultural tradition.

Traditional sporting estates are valued, in part at least, on the number of deer that can be shot on their land, and they work to grow and maintain high deer numbers so there are plenty available for well-paying clients to shoot.

To allow the natural regeneration of ground flora and woodland, it's advised that deer densities are no higher than five per square kilometre. The re-emergence of woodland at Glenfeshie in the Cairngorms has taken place with around two deer per square kilometre. On some shooting estates, it's not unusual to have forty animals per square kilometre.

There are also human costs associated with inflated deer populations. Each year, 7,000 traffic accidents on Scotland's roads are attributed to deer with an estimated cost of £5m. The increasing amount of fencing required to manage deer movements often comes out of the public purse. Forest Enterprise Scotland, the public agency responsible for deer control on Forestry Commission ground, spends £6m each year on culling and fencing.

The uniquely Scottish tradition of open hill stalking has changed little in almost two centuries

A deer stalker returns from the hill carrying his quarry using two Highland ponies, or garrons, a tradition which is now fading in favour of mechanised transport.

Our deer problem is in fact a people problem 200 years in the making. The endless miles of two-metre high deer fences that bullishly cut across endless miles of moorland are ostensibly in place to keep deer in, or perhaps to keep deer out. Either way, the fence itself is symbolic, as it mirrors the divisive debate over what this landscape should be. The potential for an ecologically richer future across much of the Highlands is stuck inside a philosophical fence. Our largest living land mammal is a pawn in what has become a political rather than ecological dispute. How many deer there should be, where they should be and to who's benefit is not so much an argument over red deer, but over different visions for the future of the Highlands.

Forest to Fork is a venison business run by Nick Richards on the Black Isle. Nick stalks and butchers the deer himself and sells high-quality, fully-traceable venison within his local community.

If we're to break through the fence, we need to see the Scottish landscape differently. We need to recognise its shortcomings and stretch our perspective further than land being valued solely according to how many animals can be shot on it. For those who love stalking, it's not going to disappear any time soon, but the philosophy behind it needs to evolve to take account of wider public interests. There's no reason why tradition can't be combined with a move towards a more rounded hunting experience in an increasingly natural setting, making full use of Scotland's community of professional deerstalkers.

Venison sales have been increasing in recent years thanks to the realisation that it is a healthy red meat option, containing more protein, vitamins and minerals than beef, as well as less fat. Currently however, only 65% of UK demand is met with home-grown meat - with the rest imported from countries such as New Zealand, Poland and Spain. Higher cull rates could go some way to satisfying this demand, whilst feeding Scotland's growing reputation for high-quality, responsibly sourced local food.

Deer have become a landscape-scale suppressor of ecological processes in the Highlands, maintaining and exacerbating the damage caused originally by intensive sheep grazing. Yet they are beautiful animals, amazingly adaptive and an essential part of a naturally functioning ecosystem when their numbers accord with the carrying capacity of the land. Deer in Scotland should be moving freely in and out of diverse, fence-free woodlands, gaining proper nourishment and trampling the vegetation, creating space for new seedlings to grow. They should be alert to the threat of their natural predators, not comfortable grazing in one spot for too long.

Alongside deer stalking, grouse shooting presents different challenges for Scotland's nature. The development of the railways and the breech-loading shotgun in the 1850s turned grouse shooting into another popular sport for the wealthier classes. The train could take paying guests close to the hills where they could bag as many as 2,000 birds on one day's shoot with their new super-fast shotguns. There began the careful cultivation of grouse moors to ensure that heather, the main food source for red grouse, would grow in abundance.

The burning of the moors to optimise conditions for grouse, continues to this day, giving rise to the scarred patchwork of millions of acres of moorland across Scotland - from the Borders to the outskirts of Glasgow, and the hillsides of Perthshire and Aberdeenshire to the eastern edge of the Cairngorms. Intensively managed, they exclude the full diversity of trees, plants and other wildlife that could be thriving there.

Grouse moors and deer forests cover around 5 million acres of land - around a quarter of Scotland's total land mass. The percentage of land given to nature on the other hand is tiny. Our National Nature Reserves cover less than 1.5% of the country. Charitable conservation organisations between them own roughly 378,000 acres - less than one tenth of the area set aside for hunting. Some private land is now dedicated to restoring healthy ecosystems, but it's altogether small stuff in comparison. Despite many good intentions, nature is not functioning at a meaningful scale in Scotland.

As people understand more about what's going on, particularly against a background of climate change and declining biodiversity, there are louder calls for change. Driven grouse shooting has already been in the spotlight: for the sheer scale of red grouse killed when they're driven out of the heather and shot in their thousands; for the ad hoc construction of access tracks over the landscape; for the repeated burning of heather, polluting the air and increasing rainfall run-off; for the killing of grouse predators such as foxes and stoats; for the killing of mountain hares, which carry ticks that affect grouse; and for the illegal killing of birds of prey living in and around grouse moors. Persecution of hen harriers, peregrine falcons, golden eagles and sea eagles remains a stubborn stain on Scotland's reputation as an environmentally progressive society.

Shooting is a part of life for many people who live and work in rural Scotland. For the owners of shooting estates, it's an important recreational activity and source of social engagement. For some it's been handed down as a tradition through their family. For others, it's a sign of status and wealth to have a shooting estate or to go shooting in Scotland. The industry provides around 3,500 full-time jobs, which are important for the people who have them, often in sparsely populated areas with few other obvious options. Nevertheless, it's arguably a huge chunk of land dedicated to a tiny sliver of economic opportunity, especially when it impacts greatly on Scotland's wildlife and curtails alternate forms of economic activity. Should the majority of our uplands be given over to minority pursuits? This is a question that is increasingly being asked.

Red grouse, a subspecies of the widely distributed willow grouse, provide valuable shooting income for many traditional estates.

For many people deer stalking and grouse shooting is more than a job, it's a way of life. But perhaps it's a way of life that can adapt to meet the challenges we're facing. Can shooting evolve to take place in more natural surroundings, for example? It already happens in parts of the USA and Canada and most countries in Europe.

Turning over a significant portion of our uplands to nature would take courage and an open heart, but evidence from elsewhere in Europe - indeed from elsewhere in Scotland - shows that landscape-scale habitat restoration is a legitimate and sustainable land use, providing local jobs and wider public benefits.

Change is often difficult and perceived as a threat, but it can also be an opportunity. One thing is for sure: the issue of Scotland's damaged ecosystems, and the continuing persecution of wildlife, needs to be resolved. What kind of Scotland do we want? What kind of Scotland do we want to hand down to our children? What should Scotland look like? If we consider the wider opportunities around rewilding and restoring the land, we might conclude that change has to come soon. The hills will still give us fresh air, plenty weather, distant views and big thrills. They'll just be giving us more of it, while being a home for more wildlife and a source of greater opportunity for people.

Right now our uplands are falling way short of their full ecological potential. Crucially, however, they're also falling short of their human potential.

Graeme MacDonald, Head Keeper, Alvie Estate.

Rewilding and re-peopling

People have been an intricate part of the landscape in Scotland for around 10,000 years. We evolved alongside the trees and the giant megafauna - the elks and the aurochs, the bears and the reindeer, the wolves and the lynx. Our early ancestors were industrious and resourceful. They built elaborate rock shelters, fashioned tools and weapons from antler, bone, flint and stone. They erected standing stones that to this day amaze, perplex and fire our imaginations. How did they do that? And, of course, they shaped the landscape around them to meet their needs and desires - building shelter from storms, making boats for travel on loch and sea, and maintaining supplies of food and clean water.

Our impact was gentle at first. It took several thousand years for half of Scotland's tree cover to disappear. It took just 1,500 years to almost finish it off. As the Gaels settled across Scotland from 500 AD onwards they named the hills, rivers, straths and glens after the animals that lived there, or the land's resemblance to human body parts, fusing us as one in rocky promontories, headlands and peaks - sròn (nose/ridge), cìoch (breast), Rubha Àird an Tuirc (point of the promontory of the wild boar) on Loch Broom, or Eas an Taghain (waterfall of the pine marten) near Elphin.

They gave names to features in the landscape that described their primary qualities - Loch Gainmhich (sandy loch), Loch Ruighean an Aitinn (loch of the small slope of the juniper) or Fuar Tholl (cold hollow). In the Cairngorms, the village of Kingussie translates as 'end of the pinewood' and nearby Loch Insh is thought to have been known as Linn Garan in Pictish times, or 'Crane Lake.'

Many of these historical names persist on our maps today. If you can read Gaelic, you can read much of the landscape without even seeing it.

We are, like it or not, part and parcel of the landscape. We are no more separate from nature than our hands are separate from our arms. Our existence depends on a healthy ecosystem because we are part of that ecosystem. We can kid ourselves that smart houses, smart phones and state of the art cars are the essentials of life, but we came from the natural world. In fact, we're at the heart of it - the king of keystone species with a tremendous ability to impact all life on Earth. This bestows upon us a unique responsibility, and to meet that responsibility we need to understand it.

We need to rediscover our place in the natural order and work with our community instead of against it; to build instead of tearing down and help our neighbouring species expand instead of shrink. Most of us understand that we need to find ways to prosper that don't rely on the relentless exploitation of natural resources. Rewilding is about finding and developing new opportunities to thrive economically, as well as biologically, with nature.

Thriving in partnership with nature isn't a new concept. In 1951, the Nature Conservancy Council bought land at Beinn Eighe and created the UK's first National Nature Reserve. The aim was to rescue this precious piece of dying pinewood following the final assault made on its old trees during the Second World War. The late Dick Balharry, a well-known figure in Scottish conservation, was appointed warden of the 10,000 acre reserve in 1962 at age 24. He had one eye firmly on the trees, but after spending time in the United States learning how its National Park Service managed land for wildlife and visitors, his other eye was on people. He later recalled that: "This was a turning point in my life and fuelled my desire to drive change and promote the benefits and joys of Scotland's natural heritage to a wider audience, by whatever means I could."

Balharry worked to turn Beinn Eighe into a visitor attraction, starting with a small visitor centre in the trees. The latest incarnation of this is well worth a stop today to learn about the history of the area and the Gaelic words that describe its landscape. He also master planned the Beinn Eighe mountain path. Inspired by the American trail system, this beautifully engineered guided route takes you through the ancient pine forest, the Coille na Glas Leitire (wood of the grey slope), before nipping up along the edge of a gorge and emerging on a rocky plateau. It's a fantastic walk especially when the leaves are on the birch trees in spring, summer and autumn. Pioneering in its day, it's now one of many nature reserves that work to protect bits of nature while striving to connect people more deeply with their natural surroundings.

Those of us who love being out in nature, in the fresh air, know how alive it can make you feel. Looking across distant horizons, breathing in grand vistas, spotting wildlife doing its thing, taking pleasure in the smallest of natural details and just watching the stars can help us get what Alastair McIntosh calls 'cosmological proportion'. We're reminded of our place in a magical, unfathomable universe. We grasp that wild nature gives us so much more than just the basics that we need to physically survive - air, water, food and lots of carbon storage. It contributes to our good mental health and spiritual wellbeing. At its most simple, what day can't be made better by watching a red squirrel scampering up a gnarly pine or lightning scudding across an inky sky, or a rainbow momentarily colouring a rain-soaked landscape?

Young unemployed men in Glasgow sought nourishment from nature during the Depression in the early 20th century when they escaped their small lives of poverty and squalor by taking a penny tram to Milngavie and hiking out to the hills on what is now the West Highland Way. Here they found clean air and a restoring of soul, and perhaps the option to poach fish or deer for their empty stomachs. Many of them congregated around fires to keep company and debate with like minds. The Craigallian Fire Memorial, erected in 2012 two miles into the Way, commemorates these fire sitters who found empowerment and solace in the wild. Some of them went on to form Scotland's first walking and mountaineering clubs.

Phoenix Futures takes the same principle to operate its successful Recovery Through Nature programme for people with drug and alcohol problems. The participants work with conservation charities and the Forestry Commission delivering hands-on conservation projects around the country. They report improved mental and physical health, increased self-esteem and confidence, and enhanced belief in their ability to change. This is reflected in the evidence that shows opiate users on the programme achieve a 75% higher successful completion rate than the national average.

On the outskirts of Aberdeen, Mucky Boots is one of a growing network of nurseries that recognise the benefits of outdoor creative play. With access to a large woodland with native trees, bogs and burns and all the wonder that this brings, upwards of 80% of each day is spent outdoors, all year round, providing the children with a real understanding of the natural world, as well as developing physical and social skills that will last a lifetime.

A growing body of evidence now links a disconnection from nature with physical and mental health conditions. Moreover, children who miss out on time spent outdoors grow up with a lack of understanding of the importance of nature to us all.

There's growing recognition that we need wildness in our lives; that we're biological beings who should be out interacting with the natural world. Author Richard Louv coined the term 'nature deficit disorder' to describe the disconnect with nature that many children are suffering in a world that's rapidly becoming more screen-based. Our increasingly indoor, sedentary lifestyle has profound consequences for our children's physical and mental health, and indeed for all of us. None of this should surprise us. We evolved for 99% of our time on this planet without all the trappings of modern life. As a species we're hard-wired to be in nature.

We're lucky in Scotland to have some of the best access laws in the world that allow us to get closer to nature. Thanks to dedicated campaigning by people who valued Scotland's open spaces, we can roam freely across most of the countryside. Rewilding is not about changing this. Restoring wild nature is entirely compatible with people enjoying the hills. In fact, people should be encouraged to get out into wild nature, to see what it is, what it can do and what it can be.

That's the approach Rewilding Europe has adopted. The organisation has created a loan fund to help small entrepreneurs across Europe set up and expand businesses that work with nature. It also established the European Safari Company, which offers adventures in wild nature and aims to push the boundaries of nature-based experiences in Europe. Simon Collier, who headed up the business until 2019, used to say: "One day, when you tell people that you're going on safari, I want them to ask you, which continent?"

The bottlenose dolphins in the inner Moray Firth - regularly seen just metres offshore - are one of Europe's great natural spectacles. They provide thousands of people with a close-up encounter with a top predator, an experience never forgotten.

The resettling of land, a call that Community Land Scotland has made for parts of the Highlands that lost their populations during the Clearances, can work hand in hand with rewilding. In fact, it's debatable that one can happen without the other. The Highlands didn't just lose its people, its language and its culture; it lost its most fertile soils, its ways of working with the land and a massive proportion of its wildlife.

"Rewilding to me means undoing some of the awful damage that has been done to the Highland landscape over centuries," says Professor James Hunter. "The most obvious manifestation of that would be trees, but not just trees; also the wider ecosystem that was there. In particular, reducing the types of management that came in with the Clearances - intense grazing by sheep and deer."

Rewilding argues for putting nature in the driving seat across meaningfully large areas of land. EO Wilson has recently made the argument that we need to give half of the planet over to nature to give it space to recover. It sounds extreme, but if our survival depends on it, is it really? It doesn't mean excluding people, it simply means excluding people's unsustainable exploitation of nature. If we were to resettle the Highlands tomorrow, we couldn't step back into the pastoral cattle-driven economy that dominated at the time of their clearances. Yet it's unthinkable to consider extraction and exploitation as a sustainable way forward. With imagination we can surely find ways to rebuild life in community with nature.

"Humanity's most important relationship is with nature, and it has become dysfunctional. No relationship survives when one partner just takes everything for itself. Nature needs half is a formula for respect and the recognition that our partner, nature, has needs.

Vance G Martin, President of The Wild Foundation"

The history of the Clearances, of putting profit before people, of prioritising practices that benefit a minority instead of the majority, has understandably led to distrust and sensitivity around land use in Scotland. Fundamentally, there shouldn't be conflict between helping nature and helping people. Arguing against environmental repair and good environmental health is like arguing against having fresh air to breathe and clean water to drink. We all want to live fully and in good health. You could argue that we're all environmentalists and rewilders. There will always be debate about how to get to that notional better point in the future, but there is surely consensus that a better future is worth striving for?

"If I returned to the Highlands 200 years from now and saw the land ecologically rehabilitated but without people, I wouldn't see much improvement,' says Hunter. 'Equally, if people were back and not nature I would be disappointed. I see rewilding going hand in hand with re-peopling."

We do need to recognise that our connection with nature has been broken. We can study history and draw conclusions, but we don't have a direct link to those ancestors who lived more compatibly with their natural environment. For most of us, we've lost our experience of widespread flourishing ecosystems. We can't see how our rivers meandered and moved before they were dammed or re-routed or channelled. We don't know what it's like to see herring swarm into Scotland's coastal waters. We've grown used to life without large carnivores. We can't remember what the hills looked like before sheep or how shieling dwellings resembled Native American teepees.

It seems unbelievable now that cows were driven along gnarly single-track roads from as far afield as the Western Isles to markets in Crieff and Falkirk. But what an exciting challenge to learn and work to create opportunities that allow us to live better with nature. Not to return to the past, but to have a more fulfilling future.

A crucial element of rewilding is to build rural economies that allow people to make a living by working with nature instead of exploiting it. It is said that a nice view never pays the bills. Yet wildness itself has become a commodity, and increasingly people are seeking it out and are willing to pay for it. Red squirrels, otters, mountain hares, seals, deer, basking sharks, puffins, sea eagles and even 'nice views' all support a nature tourism economy that is part of one of the fastest growing business sectors in the world. Across the world, countries are branding their nature and using charismatic animals to create the impression of nature-rich landscapes, because nature-rich landscapes are becoming major economic players. Wildness itself - the view - actually can pay the bills.

The town of Bad Schandau in Germany's Saxon-Switzerland National Park, uses lynx imagery extensively to brand a landscape rich in wild nature.

This lodge in the Cairngorms, accommodates groups of wildlife watchers, photographers and walkers year-round. The owners employ local staff, buy local produce and services, and plough profits back into rewilding initiatives across Scotland to demonstrate a tangible link between wild nature and the prosperity of local communities.

Scotland is competing on a global stage. In Europe alone, people are travelling to Finland to watch and photograph bears. They're going to Norway for eagles, to Spain for wolves and lynx, and to Iceland for whales. Scotland has a growing cast of wildlife attractions, but we've barely scratched the surface of what's possible. Nature tourism alone isn't the magic key to economic prosperity, but many different land uses can sit alongside and benefit from rewilded landscapes. These may include sustainable hunting, fishing and farming, high-quality food production and woodcraft skills. People working in the arts, technology, communications and numerous other professions may be attracted to live in areas with good recreational opportunities in flourishing, healthy nature; landscapes that local people are connected with.

We also need to consider the human cost of not rewilding. In the face of climate change, can we afford not to restore our precious peatlands, which store more carbon than tropical rainforests? Perhaps we should be paying landowners to store carbon on our behalf or paying farmers to 'produce' biodiversity. Can we afford not to rewild our uplands knowing that if we leave them bare, the potential for downstream flooding dramatically increases?

If we can't find ways to thrive with nature then our future is in jeopardy. A nature-depleted Scotland has an inevitable human cost. As Theodore Roosevelt said to the American people in 1910, amid mass exploitation of their continent's natural resources: "I recognize the right of this generation to develop and use the natural resources of our land; but I do not recognize the right to waste them, or to rob, by wasteful use, the generations that come after us." If we can address land ownership issues and take bold decisions to help nature regain a foothold, a wilder Scotland can also be a prosperous Scotland for everyone living now, and those still to be born.

Our existence depends on a healthy ecosystem because we are part of that ecosystem.

The Falls of Clyde, South Lanarkshire. More frequent flooding events in recent years remind us that the flow of our rivers reflects the landscapes that surround them. The consequences of rain and snow-melt cascading off bare hills and glens unable to retain water, are obvious.

The value of wilderness by Stevie Christie

Stevie Christie is co-owner and Head of Adventure at adventure travel company, Wilderness Scotland, which has twice been named the World's Leading Green Tour Operator at the World Travel Awards.

A well-known line from Sorley MacLean's poem 'The Island' reads: *And even if I came in sight of paradise, what price its moon without Blaven?*

I have no idea what the moon in paradise is worth in economic terms, but I'm willing to bet that it has a value. And as Sorley Maclean identified, even if not in strictly economic terms, its value would be enhanced by wild land and a beautiful view.

While that may be an artistic interpretation, he's not alone in thinking this – the housing market agrees. Take two similar houses in a similar location - but give one of them an open outlook across a park. Suddenly it will be more desirable and consequently, have a greater value. Give that same house a view over the sea, or over mountains, and its value will increase further still.

The same is true in tourism. Wilderness lodges in Alaska and safari camps across Africa regularly charge more than $4,000 per couple per night. Of course, they are luxurious – but a safari tent in the wilderness is never going to compete with the traditional luxury you'd find in a 5-star hotel in any capital city. So why does a luxurious suite at The Balmoral in Edinburgh cost half the price of a tented camp in Kenya?

If it was purely down to location and land value, a city centre hotel would charge more every time. If it is simply because of the wild animals, why can a wilderness lodge in Alaska charge the same as the tented camp? In fact, the true selling point of these locations is the wilderness that surrounds them. Everything else is complementary. Tourism economies across the globe are flourishing because they have recognised that in an age of over-connectedness and busy lives, having the space and time to think and to truly relax is the highest form of luxury - and one that people will pay a premium for.

Let's consider tourism in Scotland. Time and time again we hear from VisitScotland that the number one reason for people visiting Scotland is 'the unspoilt scenery'. The key word here is 'unspoilt'. There's no doubt that the landscape in Scotland, particularly in the Highlands and Islands, is incredibly beautiful. However, there are many other landscapes across the world that can compete with it. One such competitor – especially when trying to attract high-value tourists from North America – are the Alps.

So why would someone choose Scotland over the Alps for their trip to Europe? There's no doubt that the Alps are stunning and perhaps more spectacular than the Highlands. However, travel through the valleys of the Alps and you are hard-pushed to find wilderness. As well as the busy towns, you'll find power stations and pylons everywhere. Even if you climb to the higher elevations, the views are interrupted by cable cars. The scenery is beautiful, wild even – but it's not wilderness.

I regularly hear from high-end clients that while they want to stay in 5-star properties, they also want to get into real wilderness. As well as being prepared to forego traditional luxury, they're also willing to pay a premium for getting into what they deem to be pristine wilderness.

It seems clear then that wilderness has economic value. That being the case, however, then the converse must also be true – that if you make land less wild, you diminish its value economically. And the opposite would also apply – that if you make wild land wilder, you enhance its economic value.

Scotland is blessed with wild landscapes that visitors from across the world come to see. Why then would we do anything to put this key national resource at risk? Why would we build wind turbines and towering pylons in wild landscapes when they could be built closer to the population centres that require the energy? Is the short-term financial gain worth the long-term damage to one of Scotland's key economic assets – its wild land?

The Scottish Government acknowledges that tourism is one of Scotland's key business sectors and that wild land is its key asset. To position Scotland as a global destination for tourism, we don't need a new way of thinking, we just need to start applying what we already know – that wilderness adds value, and that we need to protect and invest in this valuable economic resource.

Scotland's wilderness cannot compare with the sheer scale of the landscapes of Alaska or parts of Africa. But rewilding offers the chance to compete on the quality of that wilderness. Imagine if we started investing in Scotland's wild places - removing pylons, restoring bulldozed hill tracks, refilling remote glens with native trees and plants, even animals. The process of rewilding would create many jobs in the short and medium-term. But the longer-term outcome would be a significant enhancement in the value of Scotland's wild places; an economic value which would be realised by attracting higher-spending tourists and through the creation of better-paid jobs in a sustainable sector of Scotland's economy.

Scotland is blessed with landscapes that provide the backbone for its tourism industry. However, to give our tourism sector the chance to realise its full potential, we need to protect, invest in and rewild these landscapes. Doing this would allow Scotland to compete in a global marketplace where wild land is valued as the ultimate luxury travel experience. Surely that offers a more sustainable future for Scotland than short-term hits from profit-hungry energy firms who, for a few dollars more, would happily build a wind farm under Sorley MacLean's moon in paradise?

The big blue picture

When a humpback whale exhales, the explosive 'spoosh' sends thousands of litres of hot, fishy breath shooting into the sea air, often condensing into a thick spray that can be seen and heard for miles around. This spectacular sight and sound would once have been commonplace around Scotland's coastline. Our rich, soupy waters attracted small fish and, in turn, huge balls of herring and whiting, which would bring these ocean giants lunging up from the depths to feed. How many of us today have witnessed such an event? It's just one small loss in the midst of many when it comes to the degradation of our coastal waters.

Around 80% of Scotland's landmass is under water. Our seas used to be home to the biggest creatures on the planet - the blue, humpback, fin, sperm, bottlenose and sei whales. And yet, like the decline of large mammals on land, whales were hunted at sea to near local extinction for their meat and oil. In the first three decades of the 20th century, 7,000 whales were caught in Scotland. Of these, 85 were blue whales - the largest animal that has ever lived. Commercial whaling finally ended in 1963.

It's difficult to imagine lost abundance. Gone are the herring, the crowded harbours stacked with fish barrels, and the rest of human life that buzzed around the plentiful seas. All now fading memories like old photographs on a pub wall. But the richness of our seas is still embroidered into the place names of our land. Isle of Muck is the Isle of the Whales. Canna, Foula and Fiskavaig all speak of life beneath the waves. Our shared cultural heritage hints not just at the rich natural history of our seas, but what they could be once again.

The dwindling biodiversity of our ocean, a de-wilding of the seas, has followed a sad and similar pattern to that on land. We hunted the big beasts and denuded centuries-old habitats in pursuit of food and raw materials. Huge oyster beds, pumping and filtering the Firth of Forth were raked out in the 19th century. We have harvested and exploited harder and harder, and in so doing altered the ecological foundations of our marine environment.

Through the centuries, steam-powered trawlers replaced oar and sail, deploying ever-more ingenious methods to sieve the sea of protein using the ring net, pair trawl and purse seine. As recently as the mid-1990s, we were trawling huge volumes of sand eel - one of the prolific lynchpins of our marine food web - from the North Sea. In one year a million tonnes of this beautiful, slender silver fish were caught, destined for Danish power stations to generate electricity.

Now, just 19 super-trawlers catch 65% of Scotland's landed fish. This has forced smaller, inshore boats to quite literally scrape the bottom of the food web - our seabed. As quota amass in the hands of a few, dispossessed fishermen have resorted to opening up new fisheries for shellfish, mainly king scallops and prawns, lower down the food chain. These are caught by towing heavy, metal-toothed dredges or weighted nets over the seafloor, which rake up sea life indiscriminately. It has been an unprecedentedly wasteful chapter in fishing history. The interconnected web of marine life has paid a heavy price.

Scotland's coastline extends over 15,000 kilometres, an intricate ribbon of sea lochs, estuaries, dune systems and rocky foreshores.

Our seabed, almost everywhere, was once alive. Muds were hoaching with worms, crabs and delicate sea pens. Reefs and sands were covered in sponges and corals. This life gives our seabed structure, which provides the foundation for a healthy marine ecosystem. Scotland's seabed is home to a mosaic of different habitats.

The east coast firths, once holding massive oyster beds, are now shallow muds and gravels. Further offshore, sand banks provide the perfect habitat for flat fish and sand eels. All along the west coast, and in Shetland and Orkney, the different rocks, the currents and waves and the impact of the last Ice Age have meant the seabed is more varied. Deep sea lochs hold steep shelves of shells, sponges and coral-like species above the muddy depths. Beyond the mouths of these sheltered waters, sands and gravels surround the islands, providing important spawning grounds for the embattled herring, while strong tidal currents lead to an upwelling of plankton that attracts basking sharks in the summer.

If you take a walk to the shore, you can be forgiven for thinking that our seabed is in good health. The nooks and crannies of our sea lochs and firths still shelter life on the margins, with rocky shores often fringed with kelp and sandy bays freckled with molluscs. But for those who move even a little beyond these shallower waters, the lasting scars of industrial activity are all too visible. A Scottish scallop diver gave this account of diving in Loch Eishort on Skye in 2016:

"That night we stayed at Heast and today we worked our way out the south shore of Eishort. We did nine dives, and on every one we saw the same level of devastation. I did my last dive this afternoon on the mark that we had left last June where the ground was recovering and looking in good shape. I found that it had been dredged heavily. It was no surprise. I was moved to the point of tears by what I saw there. I don't need to describe it to you. I don't know if I have the words. The place was fresh in my mind from the last time I had dived it and has been ruined beyond recognition with the 'ploughed field' scenario heavily evident."

Peterhead remains one of Scotland's busiest fishing ports but the abundance of marine life that once supported many more coastal communities, is now hugely diminished.

Over recent decades, we have scraped away much of the complex life from vast swathes of the seabed. The fragments that remain are our link to the past, but also to our future, because the last vestiges of mussel beds and oyster reefs could once again seed and recolonise our coastline. If we can let them do so.

Knowing and seeing are not the same. For most, this degradation of habitat has happened slowly, imperceptibly, like the creeping concrete that expands our cities ever outwards. Just as the forested Green Glen of Glaschu is almost unimaginable for Glaswegians, the decline of our seas from historical abundance is hard to fathom. Heightened awareness is incremental and often bittersweet, with some events bringing it into painfully sharp relief. On 5th January 1993, the MV Braer ran aground and spilled almost 85,000 tonnes of crude oil into Sheltand's coastal waters. It was an unarguable environmental disaster.

The march of marine industry in Scotland has brought us closer to the ocean, but is also disrupting our connection with it. As we work at sea in ever greater numbers, on rigs and fish farms, we are fundamentally transforming the marine environment. Over-intensive salmon farming, which now dominates western sea lochs, has contributed to devastating declines of our native wild salmon. Industrial noise is a hidden threat as severe as the damage wreaked by dredging. Life in our seas depends on sound to communicate, navigate, feed and socialise. The persistent, growling hum of engines and thunder from offshore developments have disrupted ancient migratory pathways, meeting places and hunting grounds for dolphins and whales. A once rich wilderness, thronging with clicks, whistles and whale song, is unravelling.

An unusually high proportion of Scotland's otters feed almost exclusively in the sea. This individual has taken advantage of the glut in food, which arrives each spring as seabirds return to breed.

The dwindling biodiversity of our ocean,
a de-wilding of the seas, has followed a sad
and similar pattern to that on land.

Slowly but surely countries across the world have woken up to this underwater crisis. New Zealand was one of the first to set up marine protected areas (MPAs), but other governments have been slow to respond. Some Scots took matters into their own hands, calling for protection of local waters with a tenacity and vision that is now beginning to bear fruit. Divers Don MacNeish and Howard Wood founded the Community of Arran Seabed Trust (COAST), and following 19 years of indefatigable campaigning set up Scotland's first No Take Zone (NTZ). This small sliver of Lamlash Bay is an area of seabed free from the pressures of marine commerce - and after 10 years it is now flourishing. Lobsters are bigger and scallops are abundant. Last year divers spotted a cuckoo ray in the NTZ. A master of camouflage, it's the first seen in the area for 30 years. COAST is now a leading advocate of marine recovery, showing by example that it is possible to turn things around.

This Common sunstar mirrors a flourishing marine ecosystem in Lamlash Bay, which is now benefitting local fishermen and in turn, the local economy.

In the past decade, the Scottish Government set out to strengthen protection of our seas through a jigsaw of Marine Protected Areas (MPAs). Covering around one-fifth of our inshore and offshore waters, these MPAs are the special places where scientific surveys have produced rock-solid evidence to justify moving or removing harmful activities. The existence of these rich habitats is seen by some as proof of nature's resilience. But unlike the land, there is so much we don't know about our seas. And while lines on maps are one thing, many of these protected areas are tangled up in bureaucracy, poorly policed and provide few safeguards against damage. They are not enough.

On 19th April 2017, a group of divers at Loch Carron returned to a favourite diving spot that had been towed over by a nomadic scallop dredger. Over the course of two weeks, the vessel had dredged across a reef famous for flame shells - all for a few sacks of scallops. Flame shells are wonderful creatures with bright orange filter-feeding tendrils, which knit together to form a carpet-like covering of the seabed. The resulting beds, which can be extensive, are a haven for sea life. Dredging across flame shells is similar to logging a patch of old Caledonian pine forest. Yet in this case, it was entirely legal. Outraged, the divers documented the damage and Loch Carron's reef is now safeguarded as a protected area.

Loch Carron rang the alarm bell, triggering growing calls to manage our seabed for a broader recovery and to recognise the moral imperative to act for a richer marine ecology. Divers have become our eyes and our conscience; our link to the daily damage still inflicted on what is left of our seabed habitats.

The more research we do, the more we discover what we have lost. Native oysters were once common around Scotland's coasts, with huge beds in our wide eastern firths and sheltered west coast sea lochs. The Firth of Forth, widely understood to have been the largest oyster bed anywhere in the world, covering more than 150 square kilometres, is now devoid of oysters.

Oyster habitats evolved in our seas over millennia and deliver huge benefits. Each oyster is capable of filtering 240 litres of water a day. They are the organs of our sea, cleaning our waters, cycling nutrients and helping protect against coastal erosion. Countries around the world are now investing in the restoration of oyster reefs and other habitats. They are just one of an array of underwater habitats that should be thriving, including seagrass meadows, flame shell reefs, blue mussel beds and rich, sandy gravels that all play a vital role.

Relict management is no longer enough. Our seas are not a natural museum to be curated, they are a place for life to flourish. Thankfully a new generation of marine advocates are taking the lead, with COAST's experience inspiring many community groups across Scotland to take a stronger interest in their local waters. The Wester Ross MPA, once doubted by fishermen, is beginning to prove itself, with promising catches reported since a ban on scallop dredging was introduced. Communities in the area are working with fishermen to monitor the changes on the seafloor, a vital part of the restoration journey.

Other countries have banned damaging fishing throughout their inshore waters. In places like Cambodia, where the marine ecosystem has been decimated by illegal and destructive fishing, locals are creating conservation structures on the seabed that deter illegal trawling (as bottom-dragged nets are snagged on them), but which also act as artificial reefs. The locals are seeding these structures with shellfish spat, enhancing water filtration and providing new economic opportunities for communities.

In the United States, oyster bed restoration is becoming a big deal, with projects in New York, Florida and South Carolina all sharing the same mission to restore oyster habitat. In Europe, the introduction of seagrass mats is being trialled, to replenish meadows of this shallow nursery habitat that is home to species like seahorses, some of the most sensitive and beautiful creatures in our coastal waters. These subsea beacons of hope are rewilding in action.

And closer to home in the Dornoch Firth, the first major experiment in oyster regeneration is under way, via an alliance of conservationists, scientists, and a whisky distillery. If successful it will provide a proof of concept that could be replicated around our shores. As one team of scientists recently concluded, restoring oyster beds is a concept that will require a complete shift in conservation baselines.

This shift is happening and it is happening fast. The rising tide of plastic pollution is stark, slap-in-the-face proof of humankind's impact on our sea. Images of an albatross choked with plastic toys and bottle caps, the Great Pacific Garbage Patch, or Clyde prawns ingesting monofilament plastics cannot be ignored. Our once pristine seas are polluted by huge volumes of litter and tiny plastic particles that are carried on ocean currents and end up in the remotest areas of our ocean and coastlines.

This interconnectedness does provide a restorative opportunity. The movement of our one Ocean, which links the Bay of Biscay with Loch Fyne and the Great Barrier Reef via the fluid medium of the sea, is its vulnerability and its strength. Just as pollution spreads, so can the spat and larvae of marine life be carried on these same oceanic currents to recolonise previously damaged areas.

When habitat recovers so too does everything that relies upon it - the slow-growing pink maerl that provides perfect spawning grounds for fish, the seagrass meadows that create havens for juvenile cod. It takes time, but this is an essential and exciting mission for us to embark on. Where there is living habitat there are fish, and where there are fish the giants return. Lone humpback whales, recently seen feeding in the Minch and the Firth of Forth, are an optimistic sign of the life that can return. It only needs us to do the right thing, to stop abusing the sea and to work to rewild it instead.

Records of chicks being fed plastic waste by their parents are now widespread throughout Scotland's gannet colonies, prompting unprecedented action to counter this global challenge alongside calls for marine rewilding.

> "With every drop of water you drink, every breath you take, you're connected to the sea. No matter where on Earth you live. Most of the oxygen in the atmosphere is generated by the sea.
> *Sylvia Earle, Oceanographer*"

WILD WORDS

by Howard Wood

Howard Wood is a marine environmentalist, diver & campaigner and is the co-founder of COAST (Community of Arran Seabed Trust). He was awarded an OBE for services to the marine environment and in 2015 was the recipient of the International Goldman Prize for his work on marine protection in Scotland.

I often dream about what diving around Scotland would have been like 100 years before I started diving. There must have been a huge variety of marine species present, and of sizes that would amaze us nowadays. My first job at the age of 15 in 1969 was hiring out rowing boats to anglers and tourists in Whiting Bay on Arran. I was working for just one of hundreds of such businesses around the Firth of Clyde. Even then the novice angler would return after an hour or so with plenty of fish for dinner. A few years later I learnt to dive in those same waters seeing dozens of plaice, flounders, rays, angler fish and shoals of pollock and saithe. In my twenties I spent a couple of years as a commercial scallop diver, spending hundreds of hours gathering scallops, but also seeing and learning about the many species still present in the Clyde in the 1970s. So what would our seas have looked like in the 1870s?

It's hard to know exactly, but what we do know is the 1980s brought about a rapid decline in the health and commercial productivity of the

Clyde. The government encouraged the fishing industry with cheap loans and grants to build more fishing boats and to spend money on developing more effective trawls and dredgers. The introduction of the Newhaven spring-tined scallop dredge (invented in the 1970s) was now able to dredge much larger areas of rougher ground in what had been pristine sea beds. It was out of sight and out of mind to most people, but it destroyed important habitat for many commercial juvenile fish at a time when stocks were already overfished. When one fish stock collapsed they just moved onto the next lucrative species. And with over-capacity and commercial catches dropping, pressure was put on the government to repeal the three-mile exclusion limit on bottom trawlers. So in 1984 the last major spatial protection of our seas was lost; protection that more enlightened fishermen had demanded a century before.

A close look at the management of our seas over the past 50 years shows an irresponsible attitude to the management of a public asset.

Government ministers rubber-stamped any fishing or aquaculture initiative and turned a blind eye to sustainability and pollution issues. If they were told that it would provide a few jobs in the short-term for the 'hard done by' West Coast, it received the go-ahead. Short-term economic decisions by a succession of governments have seen what was once a West Coast bursting with amazing life, left with only prawns, scallops and salmon farms. White fish stocks are no longer commercially viable.

By the 1990s it was clear to me and many other divers that Scotland's seas needed areas left alone to allow natural regeneration. As Dr Bill Ballantine, who established the first Marine Reserve in New Zealand said to me at the time: "find me a peer-reviewed scientific paper that says it's a good idea to fish every inch of our seas".

The recent, belated designation of a network of Marine Protected Areas (MPAs) around Scotland in 2014 is a step in the right direction, but does not go far enough. What we need alongside MPAs is a network of fully protected Marine Reserves (sometimes known as No Take Zones). These would become much-needed reference areas, allowing us to properly study ecosystem recovery in unfished areas. They would become irreplaceable natural banks for marine biodiversity and improve marine resilience in the face of climate change and ocean acidification.

Ultimately, it is local communities who have the power to demand and effect change. Local people, especially the older generation, realise what has been lost and also what could be regained. We may not be able to return to a truly wild and pristine ecosystem, but there is much we can do to improve the health and productivity of our sea life. We cannot afford to wait passively for policy change - that could take another 100 years. Only by local communities organising and demanding a real voice in the management of what is legally a public resource, will we be able to get our politicians to regulate our marine environment effectively and help it return to a healthier and wilder state.

We have witnessed what happens with virtually uncontrolled exploitation of our seas. We now have to learn from our mistakes, take a step back as individuals, communities and governments and act responsibly. We now have the science and knowledge to allow our seas to recover. Let us not be remembered as the generation who could have acted, but ignored giving future generations their birthright of a healthy, vibrant marine environment. Only when governments truly value nature and its ecosystems, rather than just valuing what can be extracted from them, will humans live in balance with the planet.

All at Sea

SCOTTISH WATERS
462,263 km²

6,500
MARINE SPECIES OF
PLANTS AND ANIMALS

4 million
SEABIRDS BREED IN
SCOTLAND EVERY YEAR

20%
of Scottish waters
are covered by the
Scottish Marine
Protected Areas
(MPA) network

St Kilda is
home to the
largest UK
puffin colony

Loch Carron
holds the
world's largest
flame shell bed

Around **195**
bottlenose dolphins –
the North Sea's only
resident population –
frequent the **Moray Firth**

4,000 year-old
reefs, covering
100 km²
can be found on the
Outer Hebridean
islands of **Barra**
and **Mingulay**

The first record
of a blue whale in
Scotland was in the
Firth of Forth

82% of the UK's manx
shearwater population –
332,000 pairs
– breed high in the
mountains of **Rum**

Scotland's only
No Take Zone covers
2.6 km²
in **Lamlash Bay** off
the **Isle of Arran**

Bass Rock is
home to around
150,000 gannets –
the world's largest colony

Puffins can live to over
30 years old
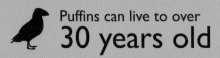

Ocean quahog can live to over
400 years old

More than **800**
of Scottish islands are uninhabited

UNDER PRESSURE

Between 1991 and 2014 breeding seabirds have **declined by 44%**

Almost **10,000 whales** were killed between 1900-1930 in the Outer Hebrides and Shetland

Bottom-trawling
is currently legal across most of Scotland's inshore waters

The Firth of Forth once held the **largest native oyster bed** in the world – now it holds none

At its peak **11,000t of cod** were caught each year off Scotland's west coast – **we now catch 500t**

Sturgeon
were once relatively common in the North Sea, today they are considered to be mostly extinct with one final stronghold in French waters

The minke whale is the most common of the baleen whales around Scotland

97% of all life on Earth is in the sea

Some whales can live up to **100 years old**

NATURAL WONDERS

60% of the world's great skuas, better known as Bonxies, breed in Scotland every year

Basking sharks can filter almost **2 million** litres of water an hour

Scotland has more than **140 sites** for seabirds that are protected by international designations

Atlantic salmon migrate **1000's of miles** to feeding grounds in the Norwegian Sea and south west of Greenland before returning to breed in the gravel beds of Scottish rivers

Scotland is home to **45%** of Europe's seabird population

8,000 years: The age of the oldest known cold water coral that forms vast reefs on offshore seabeds

110 species of brightly-coloured molluscs, known as nudibranchs, recorded in Scottish waters

More than **20 species** of whale, dolphin and porpoise can be seen in Scottish waters, including humpback and killer whales

The basking shark, the world's second largest fish, is longer and heavier than a double decker bus

Thinking wild

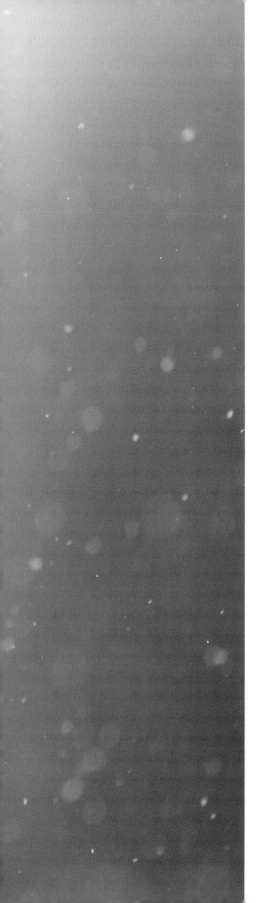

'We were eating lunch on a high rim rock, when we saw what we thought was a doe fording a torrent. When she climbed the bank toward us, we realized our error: it was a wolf. In those days we had never heard of passing up a chance to kill a wolf. In a second we were pumping lead. When our rifles were empty, the old wolf was down. We reached her in time to watch a fierce green fire dying in her eyes. I realized then, and have known ever since, that there was something new to me in those eyes. I was young then, and full of trigger-itch; I thought that because fewer wolves meant more deer, that no wolves would mean hunters' paradise. But after seeing the green fire die, I sensed that neither the wolf nor the mountain agreed with such a view.'

When American hunter Aldo Leopold shot his last wolf, something changed within him. His relationship with the wild took on a new meaning and he started to reconsider the importance of predators in the balance of nature. This is what rewilding is asking us to do today - to reconsider, rethink, reimagine. Leopold called his new philosophy 'thinking like a mountain.' To think like a mountain means appreciating the whole of existence and understanding that all living organisms are interconnected, our fates entwined with the tiniest of bacteria to the apex predator and everything in-between.

Leopold wrote this famous piece in 1949. At this time, following intense persecution, ospreys had been extinct in Scotland for over 30 years. Their return in 1954, under their own steam without human intervention, signaled something of a turning point in Britain's conservation history. This seemingly insignificant event slowly fuelled a new appetite for conserving wildlife that spread gradually across wider society. It wasn't just the osprey's charisma that captured the public's imagination, it was its success in bouncing back against the odds. The osprey's return was a symbol of hope and a glimpse into what else might be possible with a change in people's attitudes.

In the last 60 years, ospreys have thrived. These long distance travellers have become wildlife superstars with tens of thousands of people following their breeding attempts online and in viewing hides, and tracking their heroic migrations to and from Africa. In their own modest way, they've encouraged us to think more like a mountain. In less enlightened times, Scotland lost its ospreys, but today we choose to cherish them. Most of us wish the same prosperity for the golden eagle, red kite, hen harrier and buzzard, which still suffer high levels of illegal persecution.

A similar story has unfolded with red squirrels. Between 1903 and 1946 the Highland Squirrel Club, a membership group with a remit to kill red squirrels, reported they had paid out £1,500 in bounties for the tails of 103,000 red squirrels. Today these arboreal acrobats are widely adored, decorating the front covers of magazines and acting as ambassadors for nature conservation across Scotland and beyond. Like ospreys, red squirrels occupy a valuable ecological niche, but they have also helped to pioneer a new relationship between people and the wild world.

An osprey surfaces with its prey from a Highland lochan.

Motivated by a set of values that are difficult to imagine today, people took actions in the past that led to the extinction or marginalization of many species that once thrived across Scotland. If we can change our minds and learn to celebrate ospreys and red squirrels, we can surely do the same with pine martens, sea eagles and beavers - species that are all now bouncing back. Perhaps we can also learn to live alongside lynx? Changing our thinking, taking on the principles of thinking like a mountain, isn't necessarily easy. We're weighed down by prejudices and beliefs that form throughout our lives: shaped by our parents, our education, our social background, our unique personal experiences, and wider cultural and religious contexts. These factors all shape what we believe to be right and wrong, our moral vision for the world around us, who we are and what we stand for. Consequently there's often a tension between the belief that we're part of nature and the belief that we're separate, superior, here to act as owners or tamers of the wild.

In Scotland, thinking wild can be problematic because wild has come to be associated with the absence of people. This emerged out of the Clearances where it was lamented that the forcible ejection of people from the land had left it abandoned and wild. This notion has persisted through the last two centuries and has become the foundation for some of the suspicion surrounding rewilding that people may feel.

Rewilding has become something of a toxic term amongst some rural groups, with its media-driven connotation of wolves driving people from the land. Experience elsewhere however, has shown that rural communities can flourish in partnership with wild nature.

Wild is defined in the dictionary by what it's not: not cultivated, not civilised, uninhabited, inhospitable. It is hardly surprising that an aspiration to return the land to a wilder state is viewed with scepticism by many who have worked tirelessly over generations to overcome the wild and to make the land productive. But wild shouldn't be about what it's not; it should be about what it gives us. The meaning of words can change just as our perceptions and understanding of the natural world are changing dramatically. We're learning that much of nature is sentient - not just the dolphins, whales and elephants, but the small animals, birds and plants. As we've seen earlier in this book, we know now that ancient woodland is a sophisticated web of plant communication and shared resources. We are seeing that there's order inherent in nature, in the wild. When we thought we were creating order out of chaos, as encouraged by some religious doctrines, we were actually creating chaos out of order.

Nature has crafted order over millennia and as such is perfectly capable of looking after itself. Over time, the less we interfere the better it does. But as a society, we can be like that annoying manager in the workplace who can't leave you alone to get on with the job.

We won't leave nature to do its job, to do what it needs to do because we worry that it might get out of control or do something we don't want it to do. In the past, civilisations have collapsed or struggled partly through their mishandling of nature. It's thought that rapid deforestation exacerbated a period of drought and triggered the dramatic collapse of the vibrant Mayan civilisation between the 8th and 9th centuries. In Mesopotamia, increased salination of the soils, which made it difficult for crops to grow, was a key contributor to the collapse of an advanced and complex society. Our survival and continued prosperity is far from a given, especially as climate change unfolds.

Another obstacle to rewilding is the concept of shifting baseline syndrome. This describes how each generation considers the environment in which they're raised as the norm. Lacking knowledge and experience of a more natural environment, the perception of what is wild gradually changes over time so that as a society we normalise, almost imperceptibly, nature's fragmentation and the loss of abundance. We come to accept, and in many cases actually celebrate, ecological depletion. This can be seen in our perception of words like 'scrub', a reference to a naturally regenerating vegetation community. It has attracted a negative connotation while the exquisitely neat, sheep-shorn hills that subdue the emergence of scrub are held in high regard, even in areas designated as nature reserves. Our approach to national parks hasn't helped.

The International Union for the Conservation of Nature (IUCN) defines a national park as: 'A large natural or near natural area set aside to protect large-scale ecological processes, along with the complement of species and ecosystems characteristic of the area...' Around the world the national park brand is synonymous with landscapes where nature remains largely undisturbed. In most cases, visitors expect to see plentiful wildlife. The image on the previous pages shows the southern approach to the Cairngorms National Park, Scotland's largest at 4,500 square kilometres. The landscape is dominated by heavy infrastructure and open moorland managed primarily for sheep grazing and sport shooting.

The legislation that underpins Scotland's national parks is very different to the Protected Area definitions laid down by the IUCN. Like the national parks in England, they are working 'cultural' landscapes where human influence is widely celebrated and where nature has been dramatically modified. A national park where non-native forestry plantations are accepted, widespread habitat degradation is tolerated (and even subsidised under certain circumstances), and raptor persecution shows little sign of being addressed with real intent, is a compromised national park by worldwide standards. The expansion of nature and the connectivity of ecologically rich habitats is limited, resulting in a sustained loss of functionality.

If we want our national parks to sit alongside the best in the business, the legislation governing them has to change to allow for the recovery of nature, as opposed to simply maintaining it in an impoverished state or managing its gradual decline. If there is no material difference between the landscape inside the park and that outside then one is forced to ask the question: What are Scotland's national parks for? If we can't prioritise space for wild nature in places like the Cairngorms and deliver meaningful ecological restoration beyond a handful of pioneering projects; if the limit of our ambition is that of compromise, then the potential for Scotland's parks to lead the way in nature conservation and attract an increasingly discerning global audience will also be compromised.

The wildlife equivalent of 'scrub' is 'vermin.' Vermin are those species that are deemed undesirable or expendable. These are the species that need 'managing' lest they get out of control. Foxes, stoats, weasels, and some members of the crow family are classed as vermin across thousands of acres of land in Scotland, including our national parks. Persecuting these animals because we don't like them or we can't profit from them - making judgments about 'good' and 'bad' animals - is the antithesis to thinking like a mountain. It's understandable that we try to protect what we consider to be worthy, but as wildlife abundance around the world continues to decline, there's a growing recognition that we have to think beyond individual species and think about what Doug Chadwick described: "The essence of nature is a wholeness woven from infinite complexity." That's thinking like a mountain.

> " The world is not to be put in order. The world
> is in order, incarnate. It is for us to put ourselves
> in unison with this order.
> *Henry Miller* "

Ravens are recovering in range and numbers from an historical low point. This perceived abundance has led to increasing calls for their control.

Even our road verges can benefit from a rethink. These strips of land criss-crossing the country have become a final refuge for some of our rarest wild flowers and plants. Plantlife has found that over 700 species grow next to our busy roads; an astonishing diversity of plant communities. With 97% of Britain's wild flower meadows having disappeared since the Second World War, these roadside corridors of life serve as a nationwide network of arteries for myriad insects, birds and small mammals. And yet against this backdrop, the vast majority of local authorities indiscriminately cut their verges, severing those arteries. Plantlife has shown that it is entirely possible to look after roadside verges in a way that benefits nature while still maintaining road safety.

Attitudes and perceptions are everything. In Scotland, we have the challenge of boosting populations of wildlife and people - to repair broken ecosystems and to revitalise rural communities. To do this, we need to let nature work on its terms, not ours. It will need a helping hand in places to fill the gaps left by absent species, to establish seed sources where these have been eradicated and to re-ignite natural processes such as peat formation. But most of the time, it can be left to evolve on its own terms. The conflict between nature and people shouldn't exist. As Professor James Hunter says: "I doubt if anyone gets up in the morning and says I never want to see a tree again. I think a lot of the conflict between people and rewilding has little to do with the subject and more to do with the human dimension and who's advocating what. It's a human relations issue."

If people are willing to listen to each other, to understand more about each other's concerns and aspirations, we can find new avenues of opportunity that allow us to harness what the wild can give us. Just now, many of us need to give more consideration to wild nature, and many of us need to give more consideration to people. But rewilding and people are made for each other, not to exclude one another.

Rewilding is as much a philosophical shift in perceptions and attitudes as it is a physical process. Perceiving the Scottish landscape differently and seeing wild nature as an essential element of a modern, fair-minded and prosperous society might not represent an easy shift in thinking, but it's an essential one. Not many of us will experience an epiphany like that of Aldo Leopold when he looked into the eyes of a dying wolf, but we can all learn to think more like a mountain.

Wilful blindness by Ruth Tingay

Dr. Ruth Tingay has spent 20 years working on international raptor conservation projects and is the former President of the Raptor Research Foundation. For the last eight years she was been writing the Raptor Persecution UK blog, aiming to raise public awareness and to inform policy makers about the scale of these ongoing crimes.

The Strait of Messina is a narrow channel of water that separates the eastern tip of Sicily and the western tip of Calabria, the 'toe' of the 'foot' of southern Italy.

In spring 1981, a 15-year-old local girl watched in horror as migrating storks and raptors were gunned down as they tried to cross the Strait to head north to their breeding grounds. Hundreds of local Sicilian men were positioned in concrete bunkers along the hillside and were shooting at anything that flew past, but they were particularly keen on killing honey buzzards, due to a local superstition: 'He who doesn't shoot a honey buzzard each year will be betrayed by his wife'.

Anna learned that although raptors had full legal protection, local traditions took precedence and the government had no control. There was even an annual festival in Messina where the whole town would celebrate the killing of honey buzzards and any man who hadn't shot one would be paraded through the streets on the back of a truck to be jeered at and mocked by local dignitaries and townsfolk.

Anna immediately started a campaign to protect the migrating raptors; an almost impossible task for a teenage girl in a patriarchal society with such strong cultural traditions and which at the time was under the considerable influence of the Sicilian Mafia. She coordinated local volunteers to patrol the hillsides, made daily reports to the local police, wrote articles for local, regional and national newspapers, and organised protest demonstrations in the town. She later organised international raptor camps, recruiting volunteers from all over the world to come and help. The hunters responded with verbal abuse, they damaged the volunteers' vehicles, burned their protest banners, and continued to shoot the raptors; sometimes pinning notices to the corpses warning Anna to keep away.

This battle went on for about five years and the police were wholly uncooperative. Anna was dismissed as a 'silly little girl' and the volunteers were considered to be 'crazy people' who paid no attention to 'true world problems'. Law enforcement failed, not because the police were ignorant of the situation, but because they had wilful blindness. They had chosen 'not to know', either through having vested interests, fears of reprisal, or because it was just easier to ignore the problems than to address them.

Wilful blindness is all around us, on every level. Some of us are wilfully blind to the behaviour or actions of family members or work colleagues. On a national scale, recent examples of collective wilful blindness have been exposed by cases such as the Jimmy Savile sex abuse scandal, the Hillsborough cover-up, child sex-grooming rings in cities across England and phone-hacking by various tabloid newspapers. Each case demonstrates that people were afraid to act against wilful blindness, sometimes maintaining their silence for decades, until one person found the courage to speak out, often at the expense of their career.

Illegal raptor persecution in the UK uplands is a classic example of wilful blindness. Birds of prey have been protected by law since 1954 and yet some species - particularly golden eagles, hen harriers, goshawks and peregrines - are still routinely and systematically trapped, shot and poisoned, 64 years later. And to such an extent that their populations are limited by persecution. There has been a catalogue of failures by the statutory authorities to deal with this barbaric crime, not because they don't know about it, but because they've chosen to be wilfully blind. The Westminster Government still hasn't even reached the stage of acknowledging there's an issue, whereas the Scottish Government has been more progressive, but is still slow to provide an effective solution. Successive Environment Ministers have promised more action, but always on the proviso that 'if other evidence emerges then we will act'. But when new evidence has been presented, time and again, the promised action has never materialised.

The turning point for Anna's fight against wilful blindness came six years in to her campaign when the hunters firebombed her car. She had left it moments before the explosion and was unharmed, but the seriousness of the attack finally forced the police to act. Enforcement action followed and by 1990, the majority of the hunters had swapped their guns for cameras and the migrating birds were finally given safe passage through the Strait. In 1998, Anna received the prestigious Goldman Environmental Award in recognition of her achievements.

In Scotland, our turning point against wilful blindness came very recently, but only after several years of campaigning. In August 2016, Environment Cabinet Secretary Roseanna Cunningham had ordered a review of golden eagle satellite tag data, following the news that eight satellite-tagged golden eagles had 'disappeared' on grouse moors in the Monadhliaths over a five-year period. The review was published in May 2017 and its findings were devastating and unequivocal. Almost one third of all satellite-tagged golden eagles in Scotland (41 of 131) had 'disappeared' in highly suspicious circumstances, and the vast majority of them on intensively-managed grouse moors, within and close to the Cairngorms National Park. Ms. Cunningham acknowledged this was sufficient evidence for her to act and she immediately ordered an independent, evidence-based review of the environmental impact of grouse moor management and asked the review panel to recommend various regulatory options, including statutory licensing. Finally, wilful blindness had crumbled.

When I talked to Anna about our fight, she told me: "Never be blind. Never be silent. And never think that a fight cannot be won."

"
We patronise animals for their incompleteness, for their tragic fate of having taken form so far below ourselves. And therein we err, and greatly err. For the animal shall not be measured by man.
Henry Beston
"

Starting the journey

At the National Trust for Scotland's Mar Lodge Estate in Deeside, the rebirth of a pinewood is taking place. If you're wondering what this looks like, think small. The most obvious sign of the woodland regeneration is an abundance of baby trees. They're everywhere. Tiny bundles of Scots pine needles are pushing up through the heather along the picturesque Linn of Quoich, and extending up the reaches of the riverbank onto the hills beyond. The spectacular path along the Derry Burn throngs with young and baby trees joining the older granny pines, reuniting generations of a family that have been apart for centuries.

There are no regimented lines of planting here. Nature is working in its own way. The new trees gather in huddles and clusters in places they choose. The head ecologist, Shaila Rao, walks among these trees every day. She can see where clumps of young pines have come from a single parent in their midst. She can see the outliers, the lone trees miles from any other that have grown from seeds that skiffed across hard snow in the upland winds.

Her walks have taught her to expect the unexpected, and to embrace the unexpected. Ten years ago, an old gamekeeper stood on a hill looking across Glen Derry and announced, 'Nothing will ever grow here'. Now, pine trees are racing across the landscape. Foresters advised the ground on the estate would need to be disturbed to allow new trees to grow. Pigs were brought in. Scarification was trialled. But the one big action that Mar Lodge had to take to start tree regeneration was a significant deer cull. After that, the most effective action was to do nothing at all and let nature do its work. After reducing the deer numbers nothing happened for several years, then suddenly there was an explosion of green across the landscape.

"There are different ways of looking at trees," says Shaila. "I'm seeing trees spring up in really wet bog, in places where forestry experts said they wouldn't grow. They might be stumpy and twisted, but they are still trees."

A short, bent tree might not make for good timber but as a home for wildlife, as a giver of oxygen and a part of the ecosystem, it's to be welcomed. Eventually the trees on Mar Lodge will meet those expanding up Glenfeshie on the western side of the Cairngorms. Glenfeshie shares a similar past and a similarly hopeful future to Mar Lodge. Thomas MacDonell, who manages the land here, says: "Since 2006 we have more than doubled the range of the pine forest in Glenfeshie. People talk about the trees creeping up the hill, but I would suggest that if you relieve them of grazing pressure, they actually sprint up the hill. If you're focused, it doesn't take fifty years, it takes ten."

The regenerating pines in Glenfeshie are slowly reaching out to those expanding from Abernethy, Glenmore and Inshriach. This new woodland network, together with the Insh Marshes wetlands, forms a key part of the Cairngorms Connect initiative - a partnership of land managers committed to an ambitious 200-year vision to enhance habitats, species and ecological processes across a vast area within the Cairngorms National Park. It's an area where nature will be able to establish natural processes on a large scale, benefitting red squirrels, black grouse, golden eagles, crested tits and wildcats. Crucially, the Cairngorms Connect partners also recognize the role of people, as Thomas MacDonell explains: "To be truly sustainable this initiative requires local communities to see value in what we're doing. I would like to see a landscape that local people are really connected with - where they go walking or hunting or wild swimming. That social sustainability is high on our list of objectives."

(Previous page). The gravelly valley bottom in Glenfeshie is slowly being colonised by a new forest. Pines, birches, willows and alders are all putting down new roots for the first time in centuries.

(This page) In Abernethy, part of the Cairngorms Connect area, the RSPB is 'beating up' parts of the forest to improve its structural diversity. Whilst this might seem counter-intuitive, fallen dead wood and root plates provide opportunities for different species, while breaking up the canopy allows more light to reach the forest floor.

You can see younger Scots pine, birch, willow and alder on the western edge of the Beinn Eighe reserve on the road from Kinlochewe towards Torridon. This is a good example of the type of boggy land where it looks like nothing will grow, but which demonstrates otherwise when given the right encouragement and a seed source. It's the same in Glen Affric where the beautiful pinewood is expanding slowly westwards. With the consensus of multiple landowners, and suitable deer control, there's a fantastic opportunity in Glen Affric and in neighbouring Glen Moriston, to create a spectacular set of East-West corridors which would eventually stretch all the way to the edge of Kintail, providing red squirrels with commuting routes and sea eagles with flyways. Trees for Life's Dundreggan Conservation Estate over the watershed from Affric, is another piece in an ecological jigsaw that could become an era-defining project in the history of the Scottish landscape. Again, at the heart of this big idea is the revitalisation of the local economy - restored businesses built around a restored wild landscape.

Walking through a regenerating pinewood is particularly life-affirming. You can really feel the power of nature. In Mar Lodge, Glenfeshie, Abernethy, Beinn Eighe, Glen Affric, Dundreggan, these growing forest fragments offer hope for the future and fire the imagination for what might happen if nature were given the opportunity to live freely across larger areas.

The pioneering trees of a potential restored forest line up along the shores of Loch Affric, hinting at a future landscape rich in life.

Black grouse are one of the beneficiaries of the tapestry of woodland and open moorland developing at Creag Meagaidh, their numbers having risen steadily over the last 20 years.

Bringing life back to Creag Meagaidh was a choice. Following a heated public campaign to prevent the mass planting of Sitka spruce, the estate came into public ownership when the Nature Conservancy Council (the precursor to Scottish Natural Heritage) bought it in 1985. The Creag Meagaidh National Nature Reserve covers 10,000 acres in the south of the Monadhliath, north of Loch Laggan. It was one of the first places in Scotland to take a serious approach to reversing centuries of land degradation, and to enable the natural regeneration of native woodland without planting new trees. The reducing of deer numbers drew hostile objections from surrounding sporting estates, but proved to be a resounding success. Trees are now regenerating naturally up the mountainside, filling the path to the dramatic Coire Ardair rockface with birdsong.

People talk about trees creeping up the hill,
but I would suggest that if you relieve them
of grazing pressure, they actually sprint up the hill.
It doesn't take fifty years, it takes ten.
Thomas MacDonell

Bringing back birdsong is what has happened in the Carrifran valley, a grazed bare glen in the Southern Uplands. In the late 1990s, Philip and Myrtle Ashmole got together with friends and like-minded souls to plan an ambitious ecological restoration project. This group then raised funds enabling Borders Forest Trust to purchase an extensive tract of land for the creation of new native woodland. Carrifran's denuded state was typical of the area. Centuries of intensive sheep and goat grazing had left it barren. A few trees were hanging on the steeper edges of the Carrifran Burn. A lone mature rowan became an emblem of what had been and what could come back.

During the first decade of work, over half a million trees were planted on the lower slopes. More recently, thousands of shrubs and trees have been planted in the high hanging valleys to recreate montane scrub and a natural tree line. Fences are maintained to keep sheep and goats out and roe deer are culled. The results are clear to see - an emerging and inspiring sea of woodland in a bare landscape. Carrifran is now home to many different species of woodland birds that had been lost. More recently Borders Forest Trust has also bought nearby Corehead and the adjacent Talla & Gameshope estates. These acquisitions have created an exciting, landscape-scale rewilding project, 'Reviving the Wild Heart of Southern Scotland', and a blueprint for bringing back diversity elsewhere in this part of the country.

"Part of rewilding's power lies in the opportunity it offers of meeting many needs simultaneously," says Jane Rosegrant, CEO of Borders Forest Trust "The sites we work with are at their most impactful when individuals and communities engage in the work on the ground and develop their own understanding of how wildness fits into the wider Scottish landscape."

The Carrifran Wildwood in the Southern uplands shines like a rewilding beacon, a symbol of what a small group of committed individuals can achieve – this is community rewilding in action.

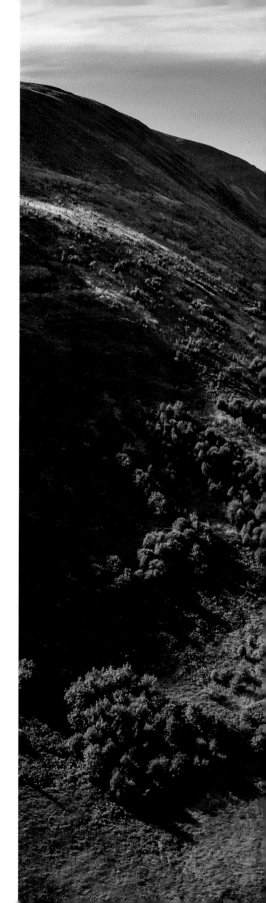

Rewilded woodland is appearing at Alladale in Sutherland, at Li and Coire Dhorrcail in Knoydart, at Corrour by Fort William, at The Great Trossachs Forest in the Loch Lomond and Trossachs National Park, at Migdale by Bonar Bridge, at Coigach and Assynt, at Glen Nevis and at the Heart of Scotland Forest in Perthshire. The work that's happening to restore Scotland's woodlands is heartening, but we need to do so much more. All of these projects combined, along with many others scattered around the country, cover just a fraction of our vast, depleted landscape.

As MacDonell points out: "Glenfeshie is a sizeable chunk of ground, but in many ways it's a speck on the landscape. We can't bring about change on our own. We need to work with neighbours at a landscape scale, neighbours who share our vision. That vision sees trees spreading much further up the hill where they merge into a montane scrub zone. It envisages rivers and wetlands functioning naturally. It sees ptarmigan and capercaillie thriving here, alongside wildcats, pine martens and of course, healthy red deer. Our vision for Glenfeshie is long-term, but ultimately results in an abundance of life, including human life."

Shaila Rao shares that aspiration: "I believe a rewilded landscape with its full range of species would be a much bigger attraction for people to visit and would have a greater community value associated with it. My aspiration is the creation of strategically linked core areas of rewilded ground at a Scotland-wide scale. These core areas will be the 'jewels in the crown' and would be connected to other core areas through a series of buffer zones and corridors."

Capercaillie are now one of Scotland's rarest birds and although their conservation is complex, it is widely accepted that they would benefit from pinewood restoration at a landscape scale, something that relies on true collaboration.

Restoring nature doesn't always mean helping trees to grow again. In the Flow Country in Caithness, the RSPB is working to restore peatlands. This hard work involves felling acres of ill-conceived conifer forestry planted in the 1980s, and blocking drainage systems that were constructed to divert water from the peat in an attempt to encourage tree growth. Peatlands around the world play a crucial role in storing carbon. They form their own unique ecosystems with water, mosses and plants their key elements. The mosses and plants absorb carbon dioxide and store it in the waterlogged peat, but when the peat is dried out or disturbed, the carbon dioxide is released back into the atmosphere. Peatlands also do a fantastic job of filtering and cleaning water, which is why utility companies in Yorkshire are working to restore peatlands there. Sixty per cent of Europe's peatland has been drained, so restoring the largest area of wetland in Scotland is a positive step.

All of these initiatives are breaking new ground in their own way. They are testing our appetite for change. Mar Lodge and Glenfeshie took a firm stand on deer reductions, something that was heavily resisted by traditional deer managers, but which has resulted in very visible changes. Carrifran tested the commitment of the local community and proved what could be achieved when passionate people come together. The acquisition of Trees for Life's Dundreggan Conservation Estate was in many ways a leap of faith, an experiment in managing a Highland estate in a very different way. These projects set out to achieve ecological change, but are now starting to deliver social and economic change too.

And rewilding is not confined to Scotland's remote hills and glens. On the outskirts of Glasgow, The Cumbernauld Living Landscape Project is enhancing, restoring and reconnecting green areas in the town. This is urban rewilding. Working closely with the local community, the Living Landscape's long-term vision is for a network of green spaces across Cumbernauld, providing clean air, water and retreats from the busyness of everyday life. Over 30 individual projects have already been delivered; from building pine marten dens in Palacerigg to restoring peatlands at Fannyside Muir. These actions are good for wildlife and good for the people of Cumbernauld.

By re-meandering a previously straightened river channel in the Eddleston Water, the flow of water is slowed, reducing the risk of downstream flooding.

Creating wildlife benefits alongside people benefits is a recurring theme in rewilding. Recognising that the quality and flow of water is directly dependent on the landscapes through which it travels, the Eddleston Water Project is exploring ways to reduce the risk of flooding in the village of Eddleston and the town of Peebles, not by way of expensive and unsightly engineering works, but by restoring some of the natural features of the catchment. Re-meandering the water course, building leaky dams - not dissimilar to the work of beavers - planting trees and creating natural ponds to store run-off water; these are all part of a landscape strategy to reduce flood risk, while improving the river habitat for wildlife and fisheries. Working with nature not against it.

Scotland's rewilding journey has only just begun. But for the early adopters, in just a few years, change is manifest. Change that offers hope. And that's what rewilding does perhaps more than anything - it offers hope. There is much to be hopeful about. Land reform is firmly on Scotland's political agenda and there's more awareness of ecological issues than ever before. Scotland isn't alone in facing huge challenges of course. As human beings, we all live under the darkening cloud of climate change and species loss. More immediately, rural communities everywhere are trying to establish new opportunities that will keep young people from moving away and sustain vibrant communities in the long-term. Rewilding isn't a panacea but it does offer that hope and opportunity.

Across Europe, rewilding teams are hard at work rising to local challenges and exploring fresh opportunities. In Portugal, a huge amount of effort is finally bringing the Iberian lynx back from the brink of extinction. Germany is boosting its lynx numbers through reintroductions. Ecologists in Poland are trying to improve the waterways of the Oder Delta to reverse the decline in fish stocks. Rewilding Sweden is working to restore rivers needed for healthy salmon migration, and to protect the remaining fragments of old-growth forests. Rewilders in Bulgaria are trying to stop the illegal poisoning of wolves, which impacts fragile vulture populations. Croatia has introduced the tauros cow to replace its depleted herbivores. Red and fallow deer have been reintroduced into the Rhodope Mountains. Bison are now back in the Carpathians in Romania.

In every country there's competing land uses, long-held cultural beliefs, a history of livestock farming and debate over the best way forward. Scotland might be unique in having a soaring deer population, but otherwise we're the same. We should take heart from these people who are working with the wild; who are freeing up space and letting nature have a go at repairing itself. Those who are avoiding the temptation to micro-manage the natural world, and who are learning to embrace the unexpected. They're thinking of the future without having a fixed end point in mind. They're befriending the wild world and undertaking to treat it well. They're learning to look that wolf or beaver right in the eye and to recognise that we all belong here, that we're part of something special. It's called life.

Making it happen

Now is a time for action, in Scotland and around the world. We've been depleting nature for centuries, now is the time to get on with rebuilding and repairing it. We have the looming threats of climate change, plummeting biodiversity and a growing human footprint to motivate us as never before. Paradigm shifts take time, but we don't have much time. We need to get started and follow the lead of those we've seen in the previous chapter, and of those around the world, who are starting to rewild and find new ways of prospering alongside nature.

On the face of it, Scotland is fertile rewilding ground. From a human population of around 5.3 million, around one third lives in just a handful of major cities, leaving the rest of Scotland's 80,000 square kilometres sparsely populated by European standards. Then take the Highlands and Islands, an area covering around half of the country. This rugged region supports a population of just 466,000, or roughly eleven people per square kilometre. With on-going depopulation of the more remote Highland areas, some rural communities are becoming ever-more fragile. Similar challenges exist across the southern uplands. We need to find new ways to reinvigorate these communities in a sustainable way, and that means maximising the ecological potential of the land, while being mindful of how people can invest in it without damaging it.

Rewilding has the promise of bringing ecological, social and economic benefits. It should be seen as a platform for reinvention, a springboard for revitalising rural areas, an opportunity to be grabbed with both hands. We can use it to revive our landscapes in a meaningful way across large areas. Many landowners and managers want to see the rewilding door remain firmly shut. Equally, some of them are indifferent to the fragile state of local communities and the lack of opportunities for young people. Still, a growing number of landowners are choosing rewilding. They think that Scotland should be a rich mosaic of joined-up habitats with natural processes determining the range of wildlife. The trick is to make this happen at scale, and to make it work for a wide range of people.

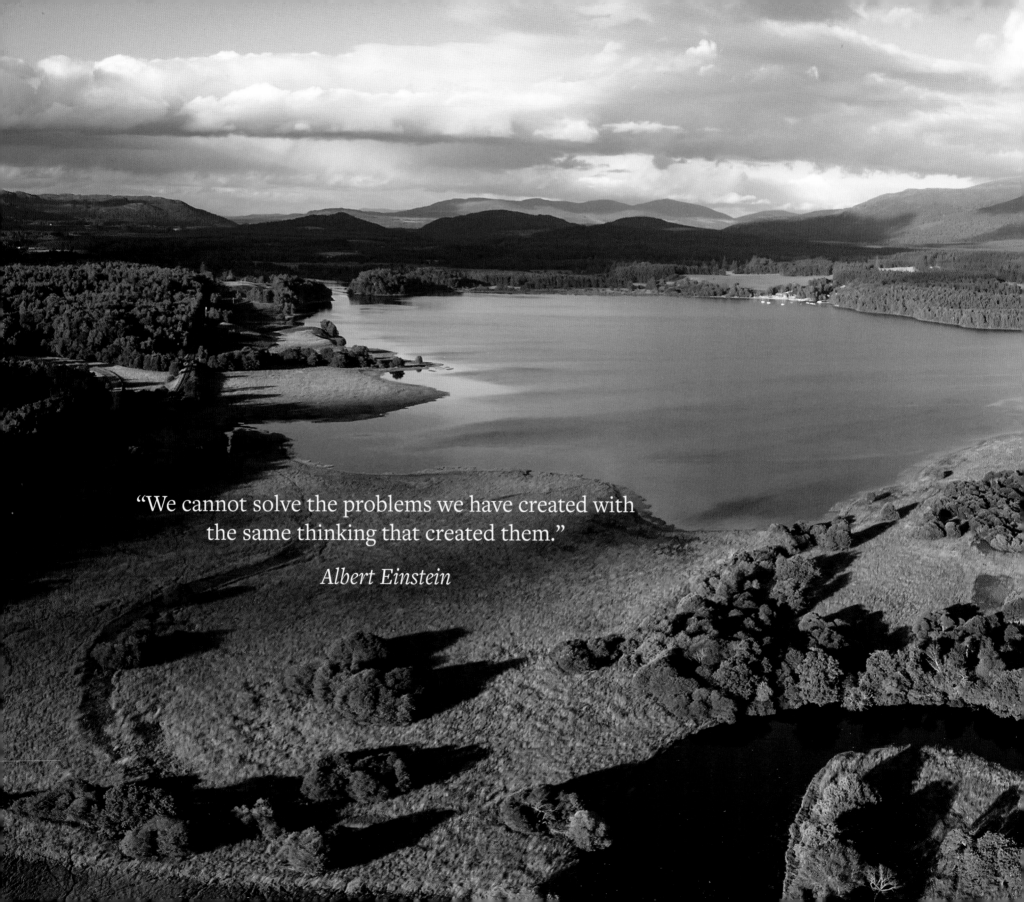

"We cannot solve the problems we have created with the same thinking that created them."

Albert Einstein

Environmentalism is breaking out of its box to become an issue for anyone who cares about our health, wealth and sheer survival on this planet. It's now inextricably linked with public health, food security, disaster management, defence and the economy. It has become an existential issue about how we connect with the land and how we want it to look. A healthy environment underpins everything everywhere and affects every single person, rich or poor, living on this planet. As Dr Cristiana Pașca Palmer, UN Assistant Secretary-General and Executive Secretary of the UN Biodiversity Convention, said recently: "Biodiversity is the infrastructure that supports all life."

Dr Pașca Palmer suggests there are three major things we need to do to stem the decline in biodiversity. The first is to shift to "an economic model that accounts for the fact that we operate within a closed system - planet Earth - and that our economic growth is limited by the ecological limits of the planet." Right now, nature is losing in a war where short-term economics trumps almost everything. The market is king.

That's a serious problem when our climate is changing at an unprecedented rate, species are being lost before they are even discovered, and the natural systems that underpin our existence are breaking down. We are taking more than the planet can give. We are heading blindly towards a cliff edge, chasing the dream of perpetual economic growth, which is close to turning into a nightmare. So this is not just about pine martens, wood ants or birch trees. This affects us all.

The second thing we need to do is stop thinking in the short-term. "We need long-term planning for the way we use nature's capital..." says Pașca Palmer. "Building a bridge between science and policy is crucial. Long-term vision grounded in solid science and short-term, practical action needs to be at the heart of our decision-making."

A golden eagle wheels away from a nest on the Western Isles where eagles breed in greater densities that anywhere in their range. In other parts of Scotland however, suitable territories remain unoccupied as both golden and white-tailed eagles continue to be illegally persecuted.

Rewilding is an opportunity to restock our natural capital, and to forge a new relationship with Scotland's land and seas that merges people's needs with the restoration of habitats and species. If we look upon rewilding as a scale, it's not possible to travel from zero to ten in a day, week or month. Forests don't grow overnight. Peatlands don't re-wet in a week. Rivers don't naturalise in a month. The biological communities that drive healthy living systems need scale and time to evolve and exert their influence.

Rewilding is a journey, and it's a journey where there are different starting points and different end points. For some, that starting point may span tens of thousands of acres of the Highlands in Scotland. For others it may begin with a section of river or a patch of local native woodland. Rewilding isn't just about the big stuff. We can all contribute to a wilder Scotland, even if it's simply creating a pond or wildflower area in the garden, building a log pile or bug hotel in the playground, or volunteering to plant trees, block drainage ditches or clear litter from a beach.

All these actions can help to change mindsets and shift attitudes to wild nature. This is the third action that Pașca Palmer deems necessary to bring the world back from the brink. She says: "Significant changes are required in our mentalities - as decision makers, producers, and consumers. Awareness and education are essential for building a common, widely internalised understanding that our planet's resources for supporting life are finite."

Rewilding takes us in a better direction, but it requires us to think differently. It asks us to overcome self-interest and everything we might have learned and taken for granted throughout our life. Reclaiming the wild means shaking off the legacy of puritanical and superior-inferior thinking and quashing any belief that suggests some species are more deserving than others, and that humans are separate and superior to the natural world. "This misconception underpinning in large measure the modern views and attitudes towards nature is at the root of people's disconnect from nature and the fragmentation we see in environmental governance and policy-making," says Pașca Palmer.

We can all contribute to a wilder Scotland, even if it's simply building a log pile or bug hotel in the playground.

(Previous pages) At Alladale Wilderness Reserve in Sutherland, landscape-scale woodland regeneration is starting to pay dividends as the trees meet at the watershed between Glen Mor and Glen Alladale.

Insect sculpture hotel

This bug house would make a lovely focal point in any garden.
Includes a viewing panel in the side so you can see what's living inside.
Made from FSC timber.

Available in the shop

rspb giving nature a home

Thyme
Thymus vulgaris
'Silver Posie'

The moral imperative now is to help nature heal. In Scotland, we have lost 97% of our natural woodland. We've drained our wetlands and overplanted our peatlands with exotic conifers. We've eliminated many species that once lived here - including all our large carnivores. We have no right to demand that other countries save their lions, tigers or wolves. We're in no position to condemn the felling of rainforests or the overfishing of seas. If Scotland is serious about its international reputation as a modern, progressive nation, then we need to walk the walk. We can't take and consume with impunity.

Imagine an ancient pine that might have stood for 500 years. Imagine its roots, its trunk, its bark, branches, leaves and buds. Imagine all the individual components of the tree but without water. Without water - the fuel the tree needs to function - it withers and eventually dies. Across Scotland there are pockets of brilliant nature. There are forests, rivers, lochs, peatlands, mountains and seas. There are puffins and pine martens, seals and sea eagles. These are the individual components of a healthy living system, but that system, just like the ancient pine, needs fuel to function. Rewilding provides the fuel that can breathe new life into Scotland. It can help us ensure that the landscapes of this wonderful country don't wither and die.

We all come to Scotland's landscapes and the myriad species within them with different perspectives, different passions and different economic interests. We're fortunate to live in a country where those different ideas and opinions can be freely expressed. But we surely all share a desire to live in a healthy, resilient environment where clean air, fresh water, safe shelter and wholesome food are a given. This is ultimately what is at stake and provides the common ground required to embark on the rewilding journey.

Scotland today is a consequence of decisions made in the past. Rewilding is a choice we have for the future. In the same way that we choose to allow land to become golf courses, grouse moors, deer forests and wind farms, we can choose to dedicate large areas to nature and leave it to work in all its beautiful complexity. We can choose life over continuing decline.

We owe it to future generations to open our minds and challenge ourselves to make the right decisions now. There is a growing scientific consensus that the next 30 years will be decisive for nature. It's in this narrow window that we will take action as a society, as a species among many, to halt the unhappy march towards a sixth mass extinction that we're currently on. Against such a backdrop, the worst decision we can make is to do nothing.

Instead, let's choose to expand our pinewoods into a grand nationwide network. Let's help our rainforests recover and flourish. Let's re-wet our peatlands to store more carbon and give our rivers more freedom to flow naturally. Let's choose to have flower-rich meadows and road verges. Let's learn to live alongside beavers and lynx and all the other animals that belong in Scotland. Let's decide that killing birds of prey is not acceptable by any member of our society. Let's choose to protect our seas and keep them healthy and clean with an abundance of life.

Let's embark now on a journey towards a wilder Scotland, with open hearts and imaginations soaring. Let's learn lessons from the past and summon courage to change the future. Let's open our minds to the bigger picture and play our role in making the world a better place for future generations. Let's make it happen.

The prize is a Scotland rich in life. All life.

> "Take the first step in faith.
> You don't have to see the whole staircase,
> just take the first step.
> *Martin Luther King Jr.*

Chapter notes

Chapter 1

Author and broadcaster, Ruairidh MacIlleathain, has recorded how many words there are in Gaelic for a type of hill.

Doug Chadwick's quote comes from his introduction to Yellowstone to Yukon, Freedom to Roam.

Aldo Leopold's quote is from his great work, A Sand County Almanac.

Professor James Hunter's quote comes from 'Wild Land, Rewilding and Repeopling' - a lecture he delivered at the University of Edinburgh on 17 May 2017.

Chapter 2

Alan Watson Featherstone reflects on the evolution of Scots pine in his essay Life of Pine.

'A single Scots pine might live for 700 years': https://www.woodlandtrust.org.uk/visiting-woods/trees-woods-and-wildlife/british-trees/native-trees/scots-pine/

Quote from the journal, nature, comes from Forests not equal when it comes to climate by J Tollefson (nature: International weekly journal of science, 4 Feb 2016).

Peter Wohlleben explains a lot about the magic of trees and forests in Hidden Life of Trees: What They Feel, How They Communicate—Discoveries from a Secret World.

See Clifton Bain's The Rainforests of Britain and Ireland: A Traveller's Guide (2015) for more on our coastal temperate rainforests.

The Scottish Moorland Group estimates in its Grouse Shooting: Scottish Moorland and Grouse Management Fact Sheet that 2.5 million acres is currently used for grouse shooting in Scotland. Andy Wightman, Peter Higgins, Grant Jarvie, Robbie Nicol state in The Cultural Politics of Hunting: Sporting Estates and Recreational Land Use in the Highlands and Islands of Scotland (2002), that "By 1957, the last date for which accurate figures are available, there were 183 deer forests covering some 2.8 million acres of Scotland."

Quote from John Muir comes from his book My First Summer in the Sierra.

The latest National Statistics on UK Wood Production and Trade: 2017 produced by the Forestry Commission for the calendar years 2013 to 2017 show that the total value of wood product imports was £7.9 billion (+6%) while the total value of wood product exports was £1.9 billion (+26%). Available on www.forestresearch.gov.uk

Chapter 3

Dr Duncan Halley related the story of the Knapdale beaver release in conversation with Susan Wright.

Quote from L David Mech was part of a presentation he delivered at the Wolf Awareness Weekend conference in Edinburgh on 15 September 2015.

Roman poet, Marcus Valerius Martialis (Martial), mentions a Caledonian bear fighting in the coliseum in one of his poems. See Art Beck, Blood on the Jumbotron: Martial's Arena Poems http://criticalflame.org/blood-on-the-jumbotron-martials-arena-poems/

Rewilding Europe shares a lot of information about rewilding actions in Europe on its website at www.rewildingeurope.com

Chapter 4

ARB Haldane's The Drove Roads of Scotland gives a good flavour of the cattle economy that once existed in the Highlands of Scotland.

James Hunter does a great job of interweaving the ecological and social history of the Highlands of Scotland in his book On the Other Side of Sorrow.

The role of the railways and the breech-loading shotgun was suggested in a Daily Telegraph article: Grouse shooting: 12 facts about The Glorious 12th.

The Scottish Moorland Group estimates that in 2011/12 grouse shooting in Scotland generated the equivalent of 2,640 full-time jobs. In 2014, the Association of Deer Management Groups estimated that deer stalking created the equivalent of 845 full-time jobs.

Deer collision costs: Scottish Natural Heritage.

The Land Reform Review Group Final Report - The Land of Scotland and the Common Good states the following regarding deer numbers: "The overall population of wild deer in Scotland was estimated by SNH in 2011 to be over 750,000 (400,000 red, 350,000 roe, 25,000 sika, 2,000 fallow). The populations of all these deer species are both increasing and expanding in their range. Adult deer have no natural predators in Scotland and the populations are usually managed by culling. The level of the annual cull of deer in Scotland has increased over the years and is now around 100,000 deer a year. This includes around 60,000 red deer as well as over 30,000 roe deer."

Chapter 5

Dick Balharry's quote is from a speech he gave at Glenfeshie on 18 April 2015 when he was awarded the Patrick Geddes Medal.

Alastair McIntosh's reference to cosmological proportion was made during a talk he delivered in Augustine Church, Edinburgh on 9 March 2018.

Quotes from Professor James Hunter made in conversation with Susan Wright.

Natural Childhood Report (National Trust/Stephen Moss) provided background detail on 'Nature Deficit Disorder'.

An engraving of sheiling dwellings on the Isle of Jura that resemble Native American teepees can be found in Thomas Pennant's book, A Tour In Scotland And Voyage To The Hebrides 1772.

Chapter 6

Alasdair Hughson, a commercial scallop diver and Chair of the Scottish Scallop Divers' Association shared his witness account adding, "Do we need to see this cycle over and again? Do the government not listen? Do they not care? Do they have the slightest inclination about what is happening in our seas? ... One week I am diving in Jura, the next, Sanday, Orkney, the next, Applecross bay, the next East Loch Tarbet, Harris. All I see is decline, apart from in the Firth of Lorn. Surely there is something to be gained from this experience?"

The Buckland Foundation in conjunction with the Challenger Society for Marine Science and the Royal Meteorological Society published 'British Marine Science and Meteorology: The history of their development and application to marine fishing problems' https://www.cefas.co.uk/publications/files/buckland2.pdf

Marine biologist Sue Scott, alongside other divers described the seabed in Loch Carron as being "ripped up" by dredging, causing devastation to marine life. The details of the incident were covered in-depth by Scottish charity Open Seas. https://www.openseas.org.uk/2017/04/26/loch-carron-no-more/

Scientists at Heriot Watt University note that, "it has previously been observed that conservation and Marine Spatial Planning usually make no reference to historical conditions, specifically those prior to the influence of large-scale anthropogenic changes since the Industrial Revolution." (2018) https://pureapps2.hw.ac.uk/ws/portalfiles/portal/16586386

Chapter 7

Aldo Leopold's quote is from A Sand County Almanac.

Gary Snyder explores the concept of wild, including its dictionary definition, in his book The Practice of the Wild.

Ali Wright said the pithy "When we thought we were creating order out of chaos...we were actually creating chaos out of order" in conversation with Susan Wright.

Chapter 9

Dr Cristiana Pașca Palmer's quotes are from an interview with Jeremy Hance in The Guardian, published on 28 Jun 2018.

Selected bibliography

Bain, Clifton The Ancient Pinewoods of Scotland, Sandstone Press 2013

Bain, Clifton The Rainforests of Britain and Ireland: a traveller's guide, Sandstone Press 2015

Crumley, Jim Nature's Architect, Saraband 2015

Crumley, Jim The Last Wolf, Birlinn 2010

Grimble, Augustus The Deer Forests of Scotland, Kegan Paul, Trench, Trübner & Co 1896

Gulick, Amy Salmon in the Trees: Life in Alaska's Tongass Rain Forest, Braided River 2010

Haldane, ARB The Drove Roads of Scotland, Aberdeen University Press 1968

Hunter, James On the Other Side of Sorrow, Birlinn 2014

Hunter, James Set Adrift Upon the World: the Sutherland Clearances, Birlinn 2015

Leopold, Aldo A Sand County Almanac, Oxford University Press 1989

Louv, Richard Last Child in the Woods, Algonquin Books 2005

Mackenzie, Osgood A Hundred Years in the Highlands, Geoffrey Bles 1949

MacIlleathain, Ruairidh Gaelic in the landscape, Scottish Natural Heritage

Muir, John My First Summer in the Sierra, Houghton Mifflin Harcourt 2011

Niemann, Derek A Tale of Trees: The Battle to Save Britain's Ancient Woodland, Short Books 2015

Pennant, Thomas A Tour in Scotland 1769, Birlinn 2000

Smout, TC, MacDonald, AR, Watson F, A History of the Native Woodlands of Scotland 1500-1920, Edinburgh University Press 2007

Snyder, Gary The Practice of the Wild, Counterpoint 2010

Wohlleben, Peter, Hidden Life of Trees: What They Feel, How They Communicate—Discoveries from a Secret World, Greystone Books Ltd 2016

Yalden, DW The History of British Mammals, Elsevier Science & Technology 2002

Reports and articles

Scotland's Native Woodlands: Results from the Native Woodland Survey of Scotland, Forestry Commission Scotland 2014

State of Nature report 2016, RSPB

Natural Childhood Report, National Trust/Stephen Moss 2012

Loch Maree: Site of Special Scientific Interest: Site Management Statement, Scottish Natural Heritage 2010

The Cultural Politics of Hunting: Sporting Estates and Recreational Land Use in the Highlands and Islands of Scotland, Andy Wightman, Peter Higgins, Grant Jarvie, Robbie Nicol, 2002

Land Reform Review Group Final Report - The Land of Scotland and the Common Good, Scottish Government, May 2014

More than 75 percent decline over 27 years in total flying insect biomass in protected areas, Plos Journal, October 2017

Wildlife numbers more than halve since 1970s in mass extinction, New Scientist, 27 October 2016

Grouse Shooting: Scottish Moorland and Grouse Management Fact Sheet, Scottish Moorland Group

Forests not equal when it comes to climate J Tollefson, Nature: International weekly journal of science, 4 Feb 2016

Biophysical climate impacts of recent changes in global forest cover Ramdane Alkama, Alessandro Cescatti, Science 5 Feb 2016: Vol. 351, Issue 6273, pp. 600-604 Europe's forest management did not mitigate climate warming, Kim Naudts,Yiying Chen, Matthew J. McGrath, James Ryder, Aude Valade, Juliane Otto, Sebastiaan Luyssaert, Science 5 Feb 2016: Vol. 351, Issue 6273, pp. 597-600

Grouse shooting: 12 facts about The Glorious 12th Daily Telegraph, 7 Aug 2017

Deforestation starves fish, University of Cambridge Research, 11 Jun 2014

Use of pine needles in sewage and effluent treatment by Manoj Chandran, Vasudha Agnihotri, Anita Pandey, Vinod Singhal. Presentation at XIV World Forestry Congress, Durban, South Africa, 7-11 September 2015

Image credits

Peter Cairns: 2-3, 18, 20, 26, 29, 33, 38, 43, 49, 51, 52, 56, 61, 65, 66, 69, 70 (all), 78, 81, 84, 95, 96, 98-99, 103, 110, 113, 114-115, 117, 129, 148, 151, 172-173, 177, 184 (2), 190 (all), 192-193, 202, 204.

Mark Hamblin: 16-17, 30, 34-35, 40, 45, 48, 76-77, 88, 90-91, 92, 94, 100, 107, 131, 152-153, 154, 160, 162, 163, 165, 170, 174, 178, 183, 184 (1, 3 & 4), 186, 196, 201.

James Shooter: 24, 36, 46, 55, 74, 87, 118, 122-123, 156-157, 181, 187, 188, 194-195, 198-199.

Richard Shucksmith: 126, 132, 135, 136 (all), 139, 140.

Philip Price: 23, 62.

Guy Richardson: Front cover, 214-215

Laurent Geslin: 73.

Ronan Dugan: 104, 109.

Aidan Maccormick: 121.

Authors

Susan Wright

Following a career as a magazine journalist and editor, Susan has been writing and producing content on nature and sustainability for over a decade. She gained a deep understanding of land issues in Scotland during four years at the John Muir Trust, and in 2015 helped launch the charity, Rewilding Britain. She works freelance and has done work for Rewilding Europe as well as SCOTLAND: The Big Picture and others.

Peter Cairns

Peter has worked as a conservation photographer, videographer and writer in Scotland for over 20 years, co-founding major communications initiatives such as Tooth & Claw, Wild Wonders of Europe and 2020VISION. He is a serving Board Member of the charity Trees for Life and a Senior Fellow of the International League of Conservation Photographers. In 2016, he co-founded SCOTLAND: The Big Picture, a charity that supports and enables the transformational recovery of nature across Scotland.

Nick Underdown

Nick works for Open Seas, a Scottish charity dedicated to promoting sustainable fishing and seafood. Having studied law and journalism, he trained as a reporter on the Isle of Arran, covering issues such as fish farming, marine planning and land reform. His interest in marine issues developed further, volunteering and working with the Clyde River Foundation, the Community of Arran Seabed Trust (COAST) and latterly for Scottish Environment LINK where he helped its members campaign for a national network of Marine Protected Areas.

#ThinkLikeAMountain

Photography notes

Nature photography can be an excruciatingly frustrating business. Hiking for miles with a loaded backpack to reach a mountain summit only for the light to be extinguished by an unexpected bank of cloud, is soul destroying. Driving to a remote forest clearing to check a camera trap only to find a wire chewed through by a mouse, saps your resolve. Sitting in a cold hide waiting hour after hour for the appearance of a wary golden eagle, can be physically and mentally challenging. You have to want those pictures. Really want them.

Gathering the images for this book, and the audio visual show that goes with it, has taken our photography team three years. Capturing the beauty and drama of Scotland's landscape and its wild inhabitants requires dedication. The team has scaled some of the country's highest mountains, dived to its ocean floors and clocked up countless hours in hides waiting for just a few seconds with an animal that doesn't want to be seen, let alone photographed. It's because our photographers do want those images that they go the extra mile.

When it does come good - when light, weather and subject do align - there's a huge amount of personal satisfaction to be had, but that tends to be a fleeting emotion. The real fulfillment comes when an image has a legacy; when it touches its viewer on an emotional level; when it asks questions; when it challenges preconceptions and when it ignites fresh conversations. More than anything, that's why our photographers do what they do: to make people think, make them talk and make them feel.

Our photographers are motivated by the desire to see a wilder Scotland abundant in wildlife, and the conviction that this will be a better place for people as a result. I hope that the images in this book serve not only as decoration, but enrich the viewer's understanding and appreciation of a spectacular country, but one that is in desperate need of ecological restoration, one that needs to embark on a Rewilding Journey.

Our photographers are also naturalists with a deep sense of responsibility to their subjects, something that is important to us as an organisation. Where required, we work under the appropriate licence for photographing rare or sensitive species and we employ the utmost care to avoid damage or disturbance to habitats and wildlife. When people are photographed, we endeavour to represent them authentically and within a context that nurtures respect.

All images in this book have been processed to represent the subjects as accurately and realistically as possible with only the necessary adjustments applied to extract the most detail from the original files. All aerial images have been captured by UAV operators that are fully qualified and approved by the CAA.

I hope you enjoy The Journey.

Peter Cairns

Director, SCOTLAND: The Big Picture